GLOBES FROM THE WESTERN WORLD

Globes
from the Western World

ELLY DEKKER

PETER VAN DER KROGT

ZWEMMER

Trevor Philip & Sons Ltd of St James's, London, specialist dealers
in globes and scientific instruments, have contributed to the cost of
publication of this book.

©1993 Elly Dekker and Peter van der Krogt

First published in 1993 by Zwemmer,
an imprint of Philip Wilson Publishers Ltd,
26 Litchfield Street
London WC2H 9NJ

ISBN 0 302 00618 4

LC 92-060242

Captions translated from the Dutch by
Jane Mountford

Designed by Mavis Henley

Typesetting by Tradeset
Welwyn Garden City
Hertfordshire, England

Printed and bound in Italy by
Sfera/Garzanti, Milan.

CONTENTS

FOREWORD

The oldest terrestrial globe was made in 1492 by Martin Behaim of Nuremberg, and it reveals a gap in the Earth's land surface. In the same year, Christopher Columbus, setting out West from Spain, landed in a region that *he* thought would be the East Indies, but which was soon to be realized as land in the 'gap' on Behaim's globe. The vast continent of North and South America had, until 1492, been unknown to the peoples of Europe and Asia.

The enormous excitement aroused by the discovery of Columbus can only be likened to the landing on the Moon by Neil Armstrong and Edwin Aldrin in July 1969. Films, models, diagrams, maps, and globes of the Moon and the space machine's journey parallel the stories, woodcuts, charts and globes of the sixteenth century.

This book, written by experts, is timely. It fills an obvious need in that there is no modern authoritative work on this important topic. Terrestrial and celestial globes are the most evocative of all scientific artefacts because it is clear as to their function: to display land masses on the former and stars on the latter. Although the emphasis in the knowledge of astronomy has changed, it remains immensely popular, as is shown by television programmes and daily papers featuring stellar diagrams.

One of the most popular of modern collectibles is the globe, because of its variation in size and attractive appearance, usually mounted in a finely crafted wooden stand. Globes are also functional, for those from the nineteenth century contain most of the known geographical features and all the prominent star positions. The collector of globes, which have always been of great educational value, has needed a book that places them in their historical context. Of particular benefit is the inclusion in this volume of a comprehensive list of makers of all Western printed globes and of manuscript globes before 1600. Dr Dekker and Dr van der Krogt are to be congratulated on achieving a clear and accurate text that is accompanied by an unrivalled selection of illustrations.

Professor G. L'E. Turner, MA, DSc, FMA, FRHistS, FSA
History of Science and Technology Group
Imperial College
London

ACKNOWLEDGEMENTS

Without the support and enthusiasm of many colleagues, institutions and museums this survey of globes could not have been made. We would like to acknowledge the advice and assistance offered by all of them.

In particular we want to thank Professor Günter Schilder and the staff of the Faculteit der Ruimtelijke Wetenschappen, Universiteit Utrecht, the Netherlands, for the hospitality given to us by the department of cartography.

Also we most warmly thank Mr Rudolf Schmidt, the Chairman of the Internationale Coronelli-Gesellschaft für Globen- und Instrumentenkunde, Dr Deborah J. Warner of the National Museum of American History, Dr Vladimiro Valerio of the Instituto di Matematica, Facoltà di Architettura, Naples, Sebastiaan S. Hesselink of Antiquariaat Forum, Utrecht, and Jeremy Collins of Christie's, London, for their great generosity in providing us with photographic material. Arranging photography in museums and private collections always usurps the precious time of curators and of the collectors and their spouses and we thank Mrs Elly Bos-Rietdijk of the Maritiem Museum 'Prins Hendrik', Rotterdam, Dr Jan Deiman of the Universiteitsmuseum at Utrecht, Dr F. R. H. Smit of the Universiteitsmuseum at Groningen, Dr Hosam Elkhadem of the Koninklijke Bibliotheek in Brussels, and those private collectors and their wives who allowed us to take photographs of globes from their collections.

We also gratefully acknowledge the special efforts to provide us with photographs made by Dr Jim Bennett of the Whipple Museum of the History of Science in Cambridge, Mr Francis Herbert of the Royal Geographical Society in London, Mag. Gerhard Holzer of the Österreichische Akademie der Wissenschaften in Vienna, Mr Grzegorz Leszczynski of the Germanisches Nationalmuseum in Nuremberg, Dipl.-Geogr. Wolfram Pobanz of the cartographical department of the Freie Universität in Berlin, Mr António Estácio dos Reis, Lisbon, Dr Allen Simpson of the National Museums of Scotland in Edinburgh, Hofrat Dr Franz Wawrik of the Österreichische Nationalbibliothek in Vienna and Dr Gudrun Wolfschmidt of the Deutsches Museum in Munich.

Elly Dekker in particular thanks her husband, Henk van Bueren, for his constant interest and verbal assistance and, most importantly, for the many lively discussions to which the making of a book like the present unavoidably gives rise.

Finally, we thank Professor Gerard L'E. Turner of Imperial College, London, for his support behind the scenes and for his willingness to write the Foreword.

Dr E. Dekker and Dr P. C. J. van der Krogt
Faculteit der Ruimtelijke Wetenschappen
Universiteit Utrecht

PREFACE

The history of the terrestrial and celestial globe extends over a very long period and includes many distinct phases. In this book we have attempted to present a general survey of the various developments that have taken place since antiquity when the concept of the globe originated.

In the study of globes one can distinguish between the globe as a cartographical document, to be placed on the same level as astronomical and geographical maps, and the globe as an apparatus, a mechanical instrument to be used for demonstration and problem solving. Rather than describing the globe according to one or other of these points of view we have chosen to organize this book around the makers of globes. It then becomes clear where and when such distinctions are meaningful within a historical perspective. By choosing makers of globes rather than users as our main line of narrative this book does not explore fully the various roles globes have played in the cultural domain. The globe as symbol for political power, intellectual status or navigation is only occasionally mentioned and the same applies to the use of globes in teaching.

From the very beginning it has been clear that our emphasis would be on the printed globe rather than on manuscript globes if only because the printed globe has dominated globe production in the Western world and particularly Europe from the mid sixteenth century on to well into the nineteenth century. The globe evolved slowly from luxury item to class room object. During this process the production of globes was taken up in many countries. In the eighteenth century globes were made all over Europe and often national conventions led to various distinctions. For instance, Dutch, English, French and American makers used different prime meridians on terrestrial globes. To do justice to national developments we have devoted each chapter to a specific country, and then chosen a theme that is in our opinion the most characteristic of its globe making industry. However, this does not imply that such themes were absent in other countries. For instance, globe making in Germany during the eighteenth century is placed within the perspective of the Enlightenment, the cultural impact of which was of course felt all over Europe.

Finally, within the limited scope of this book we have not striven for completeness: if a maker is not mentioned in this book it does not imply that he was insignificant.

ED
PvdK

Chapter 1

The Image of the World

The discovery of the sphericity of the Earth and of the
celestial sky has been decisive in the development of
the sciences of geography and astronomy since
antiquity. The concept is by no means self-evident and
how it originated is far from clear. One explanation is
that it derives from the experience of travellers
observing variations in the length of the day and of the
elevation of the celestial pole with geographical
latitude. By the time of Aristotle (382 – 22 BC) the
sphericity of the Earth, and indeed of the heavens, was
generally accepted in the Hellenic world. Once this idea
had been recognized cosmological models were
developed aiming to explain the daily and yearly
motion of the Sun and the irregular motion of the
planets. These early attempts were the precursors of the
Ptolemaic world system in which the Earth was
thought to be at the centre of a series of nested spheres
representing the planets and the starry sky. It is
probably within this rather complex pattern of
development that the idea of the globe as a mechanical
model of the heavens came into being. References to
the existence of globes are far from rare in classical
literature. It is not clear whether these early references,
if authentic at all, refer to objects that can be compared
with the terrestrial and celestial globes as we know
them today. Next to nothing is known about the
appearance of such globes; the cartographical images
of the Earth and the heavens were more likely to have

fig 1

**Detail of a Roman fresco with a sphere
(*c.*AD 50)**

*In Roman times, the globe was often used in the plastic arts
as a symbolic representation, often as an attribute of the muse
Urania. This custom is evidence of the fact that globes were
familiar objects in Roman times. On this Roman fresco, obtained
by the Metropolitan Museum of Art in 1903 from a villa in
Boscoreale near Pompei, we see a globe with meridians and
parallels drawn in clear perspective. It is not apparent from
the picture whether this is a terrestrial or a celestial globe.
The function of the pointed rod at the top of the sphere is also not
known. There is no indication that this is a celestial globe used
as a sundial, as claimed in the literature.*

been drawings on spheres rather than precise scientific reconstructions as the mathematical methods necessary to precisely define a location on a sphere were still lacking.

Nowadays, the location of a place on the terrestrial globe is indicated by its geographical latitude and longitude; on the celestial globe the stars are plotted either by their ecliptical latitude and longitude or by declination and right ascension (see pp.168 – 69). The use of such well-defined spherical coordinate systems is of course crucial for obtaining a faithful resemblance of the world. Our knowledge of the use of coordinates in antiquity is scanty [fig 1]. We do know, for instance, that the geographical latitude of a place was described by means of hours of the longest day but how this came about is not known. Less enigmatic is the use of the time difference (with respect to the meridian of Alexandria) as a means for describing the geographical longitude of a place. A list of the most important cities with their 'time' coordinates is appended to the end of the *Geography*, an epoch-making book written by the Alexandrian geographer and astronomer Ptolemy (or Claudius Ptolemaeus, AD 150). More important is that in this book for the first time spherical coordinates are described and consistently used in geography, as is substantiated by a list of the geographical longitude and latitude of some 8,000 localities. Similarly, the first star catalogue with the positions of more than 1,000 stars in ecliptic latitude and longitude is included in Ptolemy's other, equally famous work, the *Almagest*. By application of such mathematically defined data the globe became the scientific instrument we know today. It is therefore appropriate to let the history of both the terrestrial and the celestial globe as made in the Western world start with

Ptolemy. This is not to say that all globes made in the West since Ptolemy adhere to scientific outlines as described in his or later books on geography and astronomy. Globes were also used in other pursuits, as symbols and as pieces of decoration. Showpieces such as the *Atlante Farnese* [fig 2], the only surviving globe from antiquity, have been made throughout the centuries and reflect the role images of the world have played in the cultural expression of their times. Especially during the Renaissance such objects, often jewels of gold and silver work, were very much in demand.

fig 2
The Farnese Atlas (*c.*AD 150)

NAPLES. MUSEO ARCHEOLOGICO: PHOTO: SOPRINTENDENZA
ARCHEOLOGICA DELLE PROVINCE DI NAPOLI E CASERTA-NAPOLI

Greek mythology tells that the Titan Atlas had to bear the firmament upon his shoulders, as a punishment for his part in the revolt against Zeus. The figure of Atlas is a common theme in the plastic arts, with the sphere of the Earth often being used in place of the firmament. In 1575, a marble image of an Atlas figure with a celestial globe was found in Rome. It came into the collection of antiquities belonging to Cardinal Alessandro Farnese. The date of the Atlante Farnese, *as the sculpture was then called, is not known. However, the representation of the vernal equinox is similar to that in Ptolemy's* Almagest, *from around AD 150. It can be assumed that it was made after 150. The sphere has a diameter of about 25½in (65 cm) and shows only constellations, the ecliptic, the equator, the tropics, the polar circles and the colures. The constellations are seen in reverse in accordance with the rule of Hipparchus (second century BC). No stars are indicated.*

12

In antiquity the celestial globe seems to have been more widespread than the terrestrial globe, in contrast to the present state of affairs. The reasons are explained by Ptolemy himself in his *Geography:* 'The system, which locates the map on a sphere, obviously preserves the world's shape and obviates the need for any manipulation of it; on the other hand, it hardly provides the size necessary for containing most of the things that must be set in place, nor can it let the entire map be seen from one vantage point; instead, one must move either one's own eyes or the sphere in order to view the rest' (Harley and Woodward, 1987, p.185).

Ptolemy preferred another system of graphic presentation of the whole terrestrial world, by which it is projected on a flat surface and seen in one view. To the construction of such planar views and its underlying mathematical theory the major part of his *Geography* is dedicated. One might argue that Ptolemy's objections would apply also to the celestial globe. However, the scale problems of the latter are totally distinct in character from those of the terrestrial globe. Besides, the concept of a moving sphere is so essential for heavenly phenomena such as the daily rising and setting of the stars, that the globe was favoured above other ways of presenting the celestial sky. It explains why Ptolemy in his *Almagest*, which is primarily a mathematical treatment of the motions of the planets, devotes a whole chapter to it. Central to this chapter is the star catalogue, in which for each star next to its ecliptic longitude and latitude, the 'magnitude' of the star and 'its description as part of a constellation' (Toomer, 1984, p.339) are given.

The magnitude of a star described in Ptolemy's catalogue indicates its brightness. It was estimated and measured on a scale of 1 to 6; 1 for the brightest visible star and 6 for the weakest. This scale of magnitudes was used for a very long time. We encounter it on most European celestial globes until in the nineteenth century proper instruments were designed to measure rather than estimate the brightness of stars.

The constellations referred to by Ptolemy were an important means to define easily recognizable groups of stars in the sky and in particular the location of a star within the group. For instance, stars in the constellation Orion are in the Ptolemaic catalogue described as: 'in the head of Orion', 'on the right shoulder', 'on the left shoulder', 'in the pelt on the left arm' (Toomer, 1984, p.383), etc. In Ptolemy's star catalogue 48 of such constellations are recognized. Of these, 21 are located north of the ecliptic, 12 along the zodiac, the broad band centred on the ecliptic, and 15 south of the ecliptic. By the time Ptolemy wrote his catalogue most of these constellations were well defined and generally recognized. Then also most of them had been associated with Greek mythology either by adapting existing foreign myths to Hellenic taste or by inventing new ones. For that reason the precise origin of these constellation figures and their myths is confused. Some, such as Leo, Capricorn and Hydra, can be shown to be of Babylonian origin, but this is not true for all of them. The first systematic description of all Ptolemaic constellations has come down to us in a poem, *Phaenomena*, written by Aratus of Soli (*c*.315 – 240 BC) who seems to have used a work by Eudoxus of Cnidos (400 – 347 BC). Through translations and imitations of Aratus's poem in later centuries by Marcus Tullius Cicero, Germanicus Caesar, Gaius Julius Hyginus, Rufus Festus Avienus and Marcus Manilius, a literary tradition was formed which has been quite influential in establishing the iconography and further confusing the mythology of the constellations.

In antiquity the role of constellations was functional rather than decorative as is clear from Ptolemy's insistence to draw them on the globe 'as simple as possible' and not 'very different in colour from the general background of the globe' (Toomer, 1984, p.406). The reason why Ptolemy insisted on these prescriptions is that the resemblance with the real sky should be preserved and not destroyed by a variety of colours. Until about 1800 Ptolemy's advice was ignored by the majority of European globe makers.

Constellations rather than stars determine the image of these globes.

The opinions expressed by Ptolemy in his *Geography* and his *Almagest* regarding the use of terrestrial and celestial globes have left strong traces in the Islamic and medieval worlds. Today numerous celestial globes of Islamic origin are known. The oldest surviving one dates from around 1080 [pl 1]. In contrast, very few references to the terrestrial globe are encountered in Islamic scientific literature and not one copy of a terrestrial globe is known. The celestial globes made in the Islamic world depended heavily on the *Almagest*, yet, Islamic globe makers combined Ptolemy's practices with their own. One particular feature of the Islamic celestial globe is that the starry sky is presented for one definite time, which astronomers call the epoch. As mentioned before, the position of a star on the globe can be measured either by ecliptic coordinates or by equatorial ones. Both coordinate systems reflect basic features in the heavenly phenomena: the daily rotation of the Sun, the stars and the planets occurs around an axis running through the equatorial (that is, geographical) poles, but the yearly movement of the Sun follows the ecliptic. Twice a year, therefore, the Sun crosses the equator in points called the equinoxes, because then the length of the day equals that of the night. If the Earth's polar axis were immovable, these equinoxes would be fixed once and for all and the depiction of the stars on a celestial globe would have been valid for all times. However, the Earth's polar axis precesses slowly around the fixed ecliptical pole and as a result the positions of the equinoxes change in the course of time with respect to the stars. This latter phenomenon, called precession, was discovered by Hipparchus (*c.*150 BC) and is elaborately described by Ptolemy. Because of it Ptolemy designed his celestial globe in such a way that adjustments for precession could be made. He introduced a mechanism by which the location of the equatorial pole can be moved along a circle around the ecliptic pole. Islamic globe makers did not follow Ptolemy in this respect. On their globes the

position of the equatorial pole is immobile and as a consequence also the time or epoch for which the star positions are plotted is determined. Apart from one exception this is the case with all later European globes.

Another peculiar feature of Islamic celestial globes is the special way in which the constellation figures are depicted. If we think of the celestial sky as a huge hollow sphere on which the stars are fixed, we on Earth see the stars and their constellation figures from the inside, and not, as on a celestial globe, from the outside. This distinction has been a continuous source of confusion. If we take the presentation of the constellation figures on the *Atlante Farnese* as a standard we can say that the Greeks believed that the presentation of the stars and the constellations on a globe was to be in tune with what one sees in the sky. For instance, the human constellation figures, which after Hipparchus's express statement are seen face on in the sky, must face inwards on the globe so that their backs are shown on the surface of it. It is true that by turning the constellation figures from front to rear one feature of reality is lost but the main one is maintained: the description of the precise location of a star in a constellation is not changed. A star that according to the Ptolemaic description is said to be seen in the sky on the left shoulder of Orion, is also seen on the globe in the same position, conforming to that description. For unknown reasons Islamic globe makers have ignored the Greek ideas about the proper way to present the constellations on a globe. In contrast to the later European globes, which again followed the Greek tradition, Islamic globes show the human figures from the front, thus facing outwards. In other words, they are the exact mirror images of the figures as seen in the sky. As a consequence the left and right characteristics in the Ptolemaic description of the location of the stars are interchanged: the human figures on Islamic globes are all left-handed.

The astronomical knowledge embodied in the *Almagest* became known in medieval Europe through the Latin translation by Gerard of Cremona (*c.*1114 – 87) from

Islamic sources, but the first reports on celestial globes in Christian Europe date from as early as the tenth century. The outstanding medieval scholar Gerbert (*c*.945 –1003), also known as Gerbert d'Aurillac, who in 999 was elected as Pope Sylvester II, is reported to have written on the construction of the celestial globe and seems to have made one which was covered with leather. In the early fourteenth century a few works on the construction and use of the celestial globe were written. The most widely known treatise, composed in 1303, is ascribed to Accursius de Parma. Also the *Libros del saber de astronomia*, a compilatory work originating from the thirteenth century and consisting of translations of Islamic astronomical studies written between the ninth and the twelfth centuries, includes a study of the celestial globe and other astronomical instruments. In the course of the next century, when the astronomy of Ptolemy had become well established, the number of manuscripts devoted to globes increased considerably and by the end of the fifteenth century we note that globes are produced as part of an established craft in Europe. The celestial globe made by Hans Dorn in 1480 in a way marks the start of this development. Of the various European celestial globes known to have been made before that time only two have survived. Both these globes come from the legacy of Cardinal Nicholas Cusa (1401– 64). The oldest of these two, made of wood, was acquired by him in 1444 in Nuremberg [fig 3]. It dates from the middle of the fourteenth century and is designed as a precession globe, exactly as described in the *Almagest*. For that reason it differs from Islamic and all later other European globes. The second one, made of metal, probably dates from the middle of the fifteenth century and was never finished.

The interest in geographical science after the model of Ptolemy came relatively late to Christian Europe. Although a scholastic type of scientific geography, using some sort of coordinate system, was known in the Middle Ages, it was rarely employed in map making. If geographical latitudes were determined in Europe, it was for astronomical and astrological purposes, not for geographical aims. In the beginning

of the fifteenth century the collection of geographical maps and tables preserved as the Vienna-Klosterneuburg Corpus marks the transition from the scholastic to modern scientific geography. This more or less local development gained in importance later in the fifteenth century through the impact of the first Latin translation of Ptolemy's *Geography*, made by Jacobus Angelus in 1406 – 1407. The response to this translation was overwhelming and when in the second half of the century the possibilities of the printing press opened up new ways of reproduction, one printed edition after another appeared. Nine editions of the *Geography* had already been published by 1515 when the first printed edition of the *Almagest* appeared.

The geographical ideas and data of the *Geography* are reflected in the world maps and the terrestrial globes made in the fifteenth and sixteenth centuries as is clear, for instance, from the choice of the prime meridian. Spherical coordinate systems such as geographical latitude and longitude must have a point of origin. The latitude is counted from the equator, the great circle defined by the geographical north and south poles. For the longitude no such natural choice exists. The selection of the great circle which serves as the point of origin for the longitude, the so-called prime meridian, is arbitrary. Nowadays the meridian through Greenwich serves as a zero point for counting the longitude, but Ptolemy measured his longitude with respect to the meridian through Alexandria. The most westerly point of the then known world became situated at 90° from there. It coincides with the Fortunate Island, in the Canaries. Likewise, European map makers tended to choose their prime meridians to be located in the Canaries, in particular in Ferro, the most westerly member of this group of islands.

Although the impact of the *Geography* has been most profound in map making, it also brought the terrestrial globe to the fore. The body of fifteenth century cosmographical material, copied by Johann Schöner at the beginning of the sixteenth century, contains a short treatise with a set of instructions for making a terrestrial globe, in essence after the method described

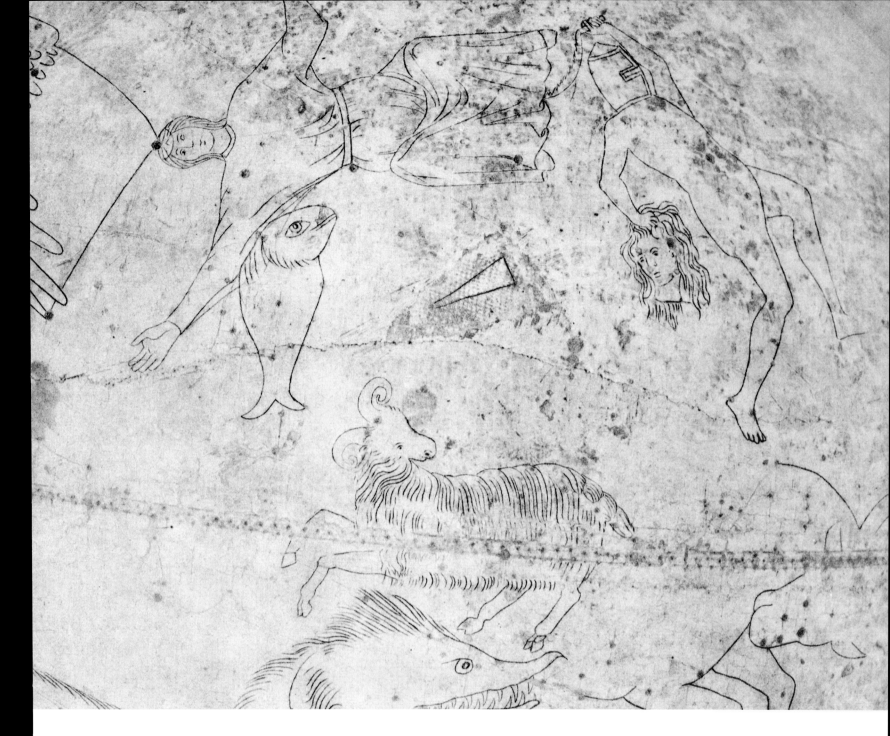

fig 3

Some constellations, including Perseus, Andromeda and Aries, on the Cusanus globe (diameter 10½in/27cm, fourteenth century)

BERNKASTEL-KUES, CUSANUSSTIFT; REPRODUCED FROM J. HARTMANN'S PUBLICATION (1919)

The celestial globe that Cardinal Nicholas Cusa (from Kues or Cusanus) bought in 1444 in Nuremberg is still in Kues (now Bernkastel-Kues). The globe is what is known as a 'precession' globe, as described by Ptolemy in his Almagest. The human figures depicted are shown from the front, as on Islamic globes. However, this is the only point in common; the figures are clearly drawn quite differently. On the basis of these drawings, the globe can be dated somewhat more precisely. Perseus is wearing a particular type of helmet that only appears after the end of the thirteenth century. The globe was therefore probably made in the fourteenth century.

by Ptolemy. The more remarkable feature of this treatment is that the globe subsequently is used as an auxiliary to make maps in equipolar and stereographic projections, by measuring with the help of a properly scaled strip of parchment the distances between two places along the surface of the globe. The treatise, entitled *Regionum sive civitatum distantiae*, seems to be related to activities of the Vienna-Klosterneuburg school in the 1430s. It clearly demonstrates that the construction of planar maps and not that of terrestrial globes was considered a problem.

The profound influence exercised by Ptolemy's *Geography* in the fifteenth century is of course closely related to a number of concurrent developments among which voyages of exploration, the Reformation, and the Humanist movement form the main features. Through all these goings-on new ways of looking at and thinking about the world were developed. As a result the practical sciences such as surveying and navigation were promoted and in their tracks also astronomy and geography. It was against this background that the oldest extant terrestrial globe was made. In 1492, the very same year that Christopher Columbus made his way to the West to find a new route to Cathay, now known as China, Martin Behaim (1459–1507), a merchant of Nuremberg, built his now famous terrestrial globe [pl 2].

Columbus's voyage was one of a series that had been undertaken to open up new routes to the East to explore new markets for trade, and so to overcome the growing dominance of the Islamic world after the fall of Constantinople in 1453. Already in 1488 the Portuguese had successfully rounded the Cape of Good Hope, the first step to the eastern passage to India. More reconnaissance of the new world followed and brought news about different peoples and unknown flora and fauna. The discoveries made during the voyages of the Portuguese and the Spaniards were kept secret by them, yet the news spread quickly via Italy to South Germany and from there over all countries of Europe and soon thereafter they were depicted, first on maps and then on terrestrial globes.

Most of the globes produced during this renaissance of cartography were manuscript globes, although this period also saw the emergence of the printed globe as we know it today. The manuscript globes, whether celestial or terrestrial, usually were made for the very rich, such as kings and cardinals, who took some interest in the sciences and the arts, or used the globes to decorate their libraries [pl 3]. Such pieces are among the most precious scientific artefacts of the period still in existence.

However, for the further development of the globe the future lay elsewhere, in the printed globes which are discussed in the following chapters. Through the methods of their design printed globes by definition fit into the scientific tradition that starts with Ptolemy [fig 4]. Such globes were produced in numbers and were used for study and teaching astronomy, geography and navigation. It is through this development that the globe became available to a much wider public and thus became the most widely used educational instrument from the sixteenth until the nineteenth century.

fig 4

The first terrestrial globe of Gemma Frisius after the woodcut on the title page of his *De Principiis Astronomiae & Cosmographiae* (Antwerp, 1530)

AMSTERDAM, UNIVERSITEITSBIBLIOTHEEK

Gemma Frisius (1508 – 55) made his first globe in 1529 or 1530. No examples of it are known to be in existence. There is a picture of it on the title page of the manual that Gemma Frisius had printed in 1530. The various parts have their names on them: 'Meridianus' – the meridian ring, with which one could set the globe to a geographical latitude. An 'hour circle' is mounted on the meridian, and over this, a pointer turns with the sphere. The part of the celestial globe which, at a set latitude and time, appears above the horizon, is the part of the sky that can be seen in this place and at that time. The 'Circulus Positionis' and the quadrant (unnamed) are aids to determining places on the globe. Next to the globe, a separate tool is shown – the spherical set-square ('gnomon sphericum'), with which one can place a 'gnomon' at right angles to the surface of the sphere. If it is set accurately, the latitude can be determined by the shadow of the sun.

Chapter 2

The Printed Globe

fig 5
**Terrestrial globe by Paolo Forlani
(diameter 4in/10 cm, Venice, *c.*1560)**

CAMBRIDGE, WHIPPLE MUSEUM OF THE HISTORY OF SCIENCE

*It was also possible to make a globe by engraving the cartography
on a spherical metal surface, usually copper or silver. These
expensive globes were only made for princes, nobles and rich
scholars. Paolo Forlani of Verona, one of the most famous Italian
map makers of the sixteenth century, made this silver globe in
about 1560 for a certain Knight Bachelor, Paulus Michaelis,
from Vicenza. He copied the cartography from maps by the
famous Italian cartographer Giacomo Gastaldi (1550 –66).
The globe is one of the few examples of sixteenth century
Italian globes.*

The arts of wood cutting and copper engraving
developed very quickly in Europe in the fifteenth
century and, since map making is a graphic art, it is
not surprising that these techniques were soon applied
to it. In 1477 the first edition of Ptolemy's *Geography*
with printed maps was published. It was far less
logical, however, to use such reproduction methods to
make globes.

The earliest European globes were made of wooden or
metal spheres [fig 5]. In the former case the sphere was
clothed with linen or pieces of vellum on which the
relevant geographical or astronomical pictures were
painted or drawn. When metal spheres were used the
cartographic images were directly engraved on the
surface. Wood and metal were also, and for a long time
remained, the basic materials for suspending the
spheres. Consequently, the manufacture of globes was
initially carried out by artisans such as silversmiths
and instrument makers. Yet, still in the early stages of
development in European globe making these
traditional methods were to be replaced by a totally
new approach, the printed globe, which during at least
three centuries became the typical European method
of globe making. From then on the production of
globes often, though not exclusively, was carried out by
map makers and publishers.

As is the case with many early inventions, it is not
known precisely how and where the idea of using the
printing press for globe making arose. The whole idea

may have evolved from attempts to cover spheres with parchment strips. The experiments made in the fifteenth century to make use of a terrestrial globe in constructing planar maps, referred to in the preceding chapter (pp.17 – 18), may also have been of influence. The first published account of the construction of globe segments appeared in a small treatise on geography by Henricus Loritus Glareanus (1488–1563), in 1527. He proposed a set of gores such that the shorter size equals one twelfth (the equivalent of

an angle of 30°) and the longer size one half (the equivalent of an angle of 180°) of the circumference of the globe. It is unlikely that this prescription for constructing globe gores was ever used in reality because then the boundaries of each gore would have to shrink while being pasted on the globe surface. In order to fit a gore to a spherical surface some amount of deformation is necessary because it is in principle impossible to represent a spherical surface on a flat piece of paper. Globe makers using paper gores must

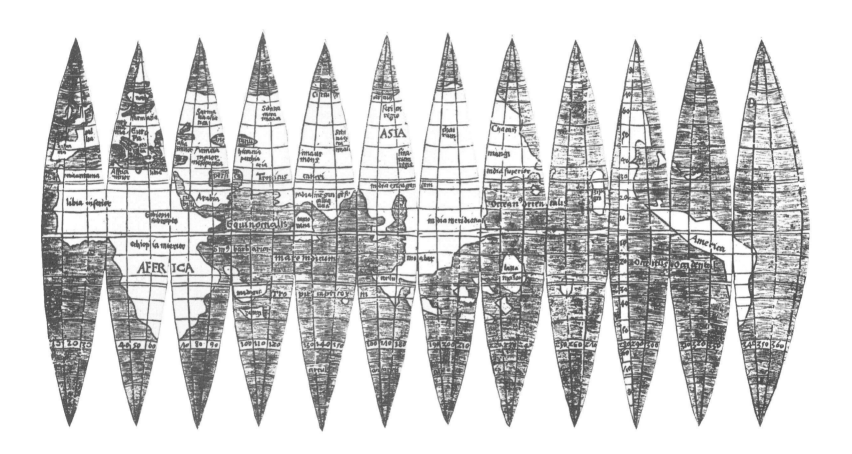

fig 6

The first printed globe gores, ascribed to Martin Waldseemüller (diameter 4½in/12 cm, probably Strasbourg, *c.*1507)

In 1507, Martin Waldseemüller (1470 – c.1520) published two cartographical works in Saint-Dié which had a major influence on cartography – a map of the world on a large scale and a small globe. The small globe was intended as a supplement to some cosmographical books written for the general public

which were printed in 1507 and 1509 in Saint-Dié and Strasbourg. However, none of the known copies still retains a page showing the globe gores. The cartography of the 'Hauslab-Liechtenstein gores' (named after previous owners) is a simplified version of the large map of the world by Waldseemüller, hence their attribution. It was Waldseemüller who thought of the name 'America' – after Amerigo Vespucci – for the new world. His map of the world of 1507 and these globe gores are the first cartographical documents on which this name appears.

have discovered rather quickly that stretching paper is much preferred to shrinking it. This implies that the longer size of a segment always has to be a bit less than half the circumference of the globe.

Globe gores were already in use some time before Glareanus first published the idea. The oldest known set is that of the so-called Waldseemüller gores, dated 1507 [fig 6]. No original mounted copies of these gores exist. The earliest copy of a mounted printed globe is dated 1515. This is a terrestrial globe made by Johann Schöner (1477–1547). Although Schöner started his career as a priest, having studied theology in Erfurt, he soon assembled a printing shop in Bamberg [fig 7]. In 1515 his *Luculentissima quaedam terrae totius descriptio . . . cum globis cosmographicis* and in 1517 his *Solidi et sphaerici corporis sive globi astronomici canones* appeared in Nuremberg. In his own printing shop he cut the woodblocks for his globes. From a letter dated 1517, we know that Lorenz Beheim (1457–1521), a humanist who after a stay of twenty-two years in Rome settled in Bamberg in 1504, bought from Schöner a celestial globe, suitable for astrological use, for two and a half guilders. Clearly by then Schöner had finished a pair of globes. Johann Schöner deserves the credit for being the first globe maker to produce pairs of celestial and terrestrial globes of the same size. Thus a new tradition was introduced in cosmography in which descriptions of the Earth and the heavens were united through globe making.

Nuremberg was the place par excellence in those days for novelties such as printed globes; it was therefore the ideal place for the poverty-stricken Schöner to offer his globes for sale. In 1526 his financial situation improved when he moved to this city to teach mathematics in the newly founded Melanchthon gymnasium. From his workshop in Nuremberg a number of copies, terrestrial as well as celestial globes, have survived [pls 4 and 5]. All these date from the 1530s. By that time several instrument makers like George Hartmann (1489–1564) of Nuremberg, best known for his astrolabes and Kasper Vopel (1511–61)

fig 7

Portrait of Johann Schöner with his celestial globe by Hans Springinklee, 1528

HANOVER, NIEDERSÄCHSICHES LANDESMUSEUM, LANDESGALERIE

Johann Schöner (1477–1547) can be regarded as the first man to make globes for a wider market. From 1515, he published works on cosmographic subjects such as geography and astronomy.

This combination led to his introducing an important innovation to the world of globe making – the production of a terrestrial and a celestial globe as a pair. The first terrestrial globe appeared in 1515, followed by the celestial globe in 1517. A new edition of the terrestrial globe, and possibly of the celestial globe too, appeared in about 1533. His only preserved pair of globes is from this last edition. In 1520, he produced a large terrestrial globe (diameter 34 1/2 in/87 cm). The cartography of this is not printed, however, but is painted on the sphere.

of Cologne, a maker of armillary spheres, had also produced printed globes. Yet, those made by Schöner have been the most influential. Their fame spread through Europe quickly as is clear from the fact that the celestial globe in the famous painting by Holbein painted in 1533 in London can be identified as one of his [figs 8, 9, and 10]. Of great importance for the historical development of globe making has been the interest stimulated by his globes in the Low Countries.

His book on globes was reprinted in Antwerp in 1526–27. And because the demand for Schöner's globes was so great, the local production of such globes was taken up by the Louvain goldsmith and engraver Gaspar van der Heyden (c.1496– after 1549), at the initiative of the Antwerp publisher Roeland Bollaert. It was in Louvain too, that the next important stage in making printed globes took place, a development with which the names of Gemma Frisius (1508–55) and Gerard Mercator (1512–94) are connected.

figs 8 ◁, 9 ▽ and 10 △

The terrestrial globe (fig 9) and celestial globe (fig 10) depicted in *The Ambassadors* by Hans Holbein, Jr, 1533

LONDON, NATIONAL GALLERY; PHOTO: COURTESY OF THE TRUSTEES

The double portrait (81 x 82in/206 x 209cm) of Jean de Dinteville, Seigneur de Polisy, ambassador from King François I of France to England, and his friend, George de Selve, Bishop of Lavour, is important for the history of globe production because of the two globes between the subjects, indicating the area of interest of the two men in the painting. Holbein painted precisely, and to almost life size. It is not known what the model was for the terrestrial globe, although it shows strong similarities with gores in woodcuts that were earlier ascribed to Schöner. Recent studies have shown that the celestial globe is certainly from the workshop of Johann Schöner.

plate 1
Islamic celestial globe
(diameter approx. 8in/21cm, Valencia, 1080/85)

FLORENCE, ISTITUTO E MUSEO DI STORIA DELLA SCIENZA

The globe that Ibrahim ibn Sa'id al-Sahli al-Wazzan made with his son Muhammad in Valencia in the year 473 or 478 of the Hegira (1080 or 1085) is at present the oldest known, dated Islamic celestial globe. The stars, constellations and circles are engraved on the surface of a metal sphere. There are 1,015 stars in 47 constellations. The 48th constellation, Crater, is not marked or given a name although the stars are represented.

The cartography is drawn following the example of the Persian astronomer al-Sufi (903 – 86). Al-Sufi's Book of the Constellations *is a paraphrase of the famous* Almagest *of Ptolemy. It shows two depictions of each constellation: one as seen from the earth, and one as it is shown on the globe. It is characteristic that, for the globe, the human figures for the constellations are shown from the front, so that they are exact mirror images of the figures in the sky. Al-Sufi's work was the foundation for many Islamic globe makers.*

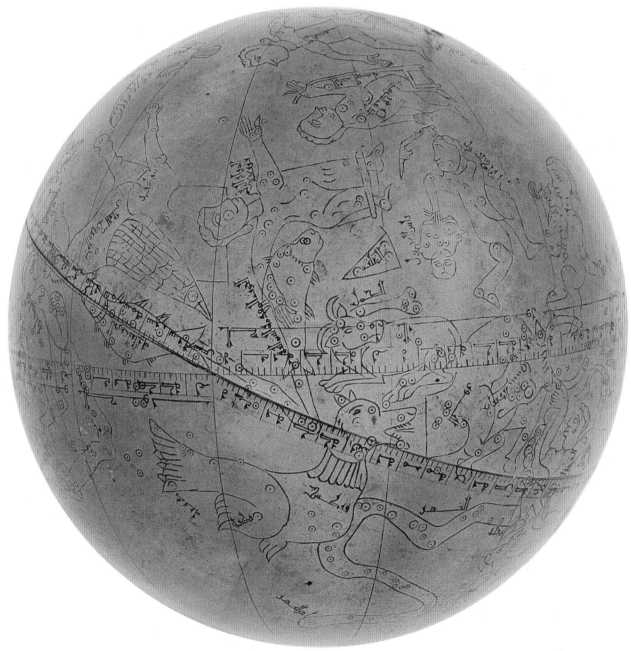

plate 2

The oldest known terrestrial globe, made for Martin Behaim (diameter 20in/51cm, Nuremberg, 1492)

The Nuremberg merchant Martin Behaim (1459–1507) lived for a long time in Portugal and had the opportunity there to learn about the results of the voyages of discovery at first hand. From 1491 to 1493, he once again lived in his home city for some time, because of an inheritance matter. In order to show interested townspeople the importance of the new sea routes and countries and to encourage them to finance a new expedition westwards to China, he had a globe made during this time by local craftsmen. His globe is the oldest terrestrial globe in the world still in existence. The cartography of it is a mixture of the ancient Ptolemaic maps, the medieval European maps and the so-called 'portulan' charts, filled with the results of the most recent Portuguese discoveries. A notable fact is that the globe has never been outside Nuremberg – for any length of time – for five centuries. It is also interesting to note that globes were made in Nuremberg up to the nineteenth century.

plate 3
Celestial globe by Johann Stöffler
(diameter 19½in/49cm,
Nuremberg, 1493)

NUREMBERG, GERMANISCHES
NATIONALMUSEUM

Johann Stöffler (1452 –1531),
a mathematician, astronomer and
instrument maker from Justingen in
South Germany, made a number of
celestial globes. One has been preserved –
the one that he made in 1493 for the
auxiliary bishop Daniel of Konstanz. All
48 Ptolemaic constellations are shown,
with the human figures seen in reverse.
It is the oldest globe on which the
hunting dogs are to be seen. It was not
until the end of the seventeenth century
that this image was introduced by
Hevelius as a separate constellation.
The constellations are painted in oil by an
unknown artist on a wooden sphere.
Immediately surrounding this sphere
there is a network of brass bands which
are in line with the various astrological
houses. There are Latin inscriptions on
the heavy wooden frame. Those on the
left tell, in hexameters, that it is man's
fate to turn his face up to the stars.
Above this, a man is depicted (Stöffler
himself?), pointing to the globe.

plate 4

**Terrestrial globe by Johann Schöner
(diameter 11in/28cm, Nuremberg, 1533)**

*The cartography of the first terrestrial globe by Johann Schöner
(1515) is very similar to the large map of the world by
Waldseemüller of 1507 and his map of America in the edition of
Ptolemy's Geography of 1513. However, the representation of
a large continent around the south pole is new. A new edition of*
*the globe appeared in 1533. New wooden blocks were cut for
the new editions, since it is not possible to make changes to
woodcuts. On the 1533 globe, Schöner showed the continents of
America and Asia linked with each other by a large land mass,
which had not appeared on the 1515 globe. With this
hypothetical representation, Schöner in turn is following
Franciscus Monachus, who published a globe (now lost) around
1526 – 27 in Louvain following Schöner's 1515 globe.*

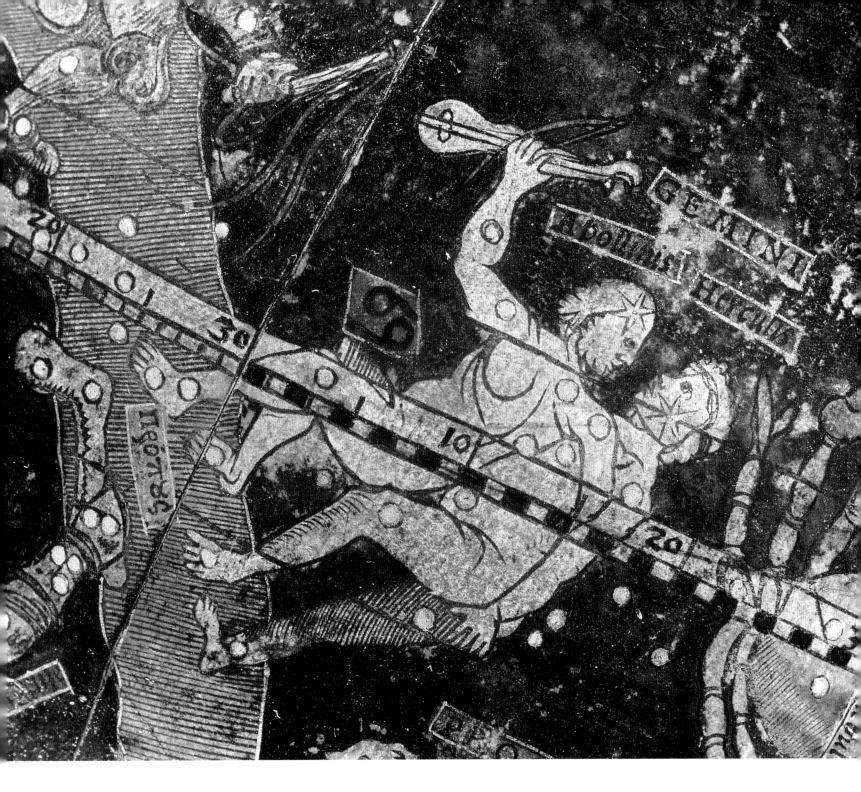

plate 5

**The constellation Gemini on Schöner's celestial globe
(Nuremberg, c.1533)**

*One of the functions of the figures of the constellations in
astronomy was to set the location of the particular stars.
The classical images were linked, in antiquity, with Greek
mythology. In order to make identification easier, each figure had
its own fixed attributes; some less important attributes might
vary. The constellation Gemini is generally shown as a
representation of the inseparable twins Castor and Pollux, the*
*Dioscures, sons of Zeus. In some classical sources they appear as
the brothers Amphion and Zethus, the mythical founders of
Thebes, with a club and a lyre as characteristic attributes. Other
classical writers identify Gemini with another pair, Hercules and
Apollo, who are also both sons of Zeus, but not twins. Schöner
adopted this last tradition, giving Apollo, patron of poetry and
music, a small violin to hold in his hand.*

plate 6

Indian Ocean and eastern part of Africa on the
terrestrial globe by Gemma Frisius
(diameter 14½in/37cm, Louvain, *c.*1536)

VIENNA. ÖSTERREICHISCHE NATIONALBIBLIOTHEK

Only one terrestrial globe by Gemma Frisius (1508 – 55) has been preserved. It is an example of the second terrestrial globe that Gemma Frisius made, dated about 1536. The results of the fifteenth-century Portuguese discoveries are shown on the coasts of Central and Southern Africa and India; this peninsula already

showed the characteristic triangular shape, with the island of Ceylon in almost the correct shape and size. The area of the South-East Asiatic archipelago is damaged in places, so that the precise configuration of the coast cannot be seen. It is clear that Portuguese sources were also used for this area, including the reports of the expedition of Ferdinand Magellan.

plates 7 and 8

**Pair of globes by Gerard Mercator
(diameter 16in/41cm, Louvain, 1541 and 1551)**

DUISBURG, KULTUR- UND STADTHISTORISCHES MUSEUM;
PHOTO: BERND KIRTZ

*The globes produced by Gerard Mercator (1512 - 94) in 1541
and 1551 mark the beginning of the world-wide fame of Dutch
globes. Mercator sold his globes in pairs: a matching set of
terrestrial and celestial globes. He was not the first to do this –
that was Johann Schöner. The popularity of Mercator's work,
however, casts such a shadow over the work of his predecessors
that, following the example set by Mercator, all later globe-
makers always produced their globes in pairs, right up to the
nineteenth century.*

plate 9

Terrestrial globe by Giulio and Livio Sanuto, (diameter 27 in/69 cm, Venice, *c.*1570)

Girolamo Ruscelli, who published an edition of Ptolemy's Geography in 1561, also added, among other things, a chapter about globes. He was full of praise about a large globe that had been made in Venice by Giulio Sanuto, working with his brother Livio (c.1520 –76), who was a professional geographer. At present, we know that there are in existence two sets of gores and one mounted example of a globe that was almost certainly made by the Sanuto brothers. The geographical information on this globe is taken from maps by the cartographer Giacomo Gastaldi. There is no name or year on the gores; however, the style of the engraving is that of Giulio Sanuto, while it is clear from the sources used that the gores were engraved between 1564 and 1574. On the mounted example, a few major decorative elements are added in manuscript, such as the animals that can be seen in the southern part of the Pacific Ocean.

fig 11
**Northern part of the celestial globe by Gemma Frisius
(diameter 14½ in/37 cm, Louvain, 1537)**

LONDON, NATIONAL MARITIME MUSEUM

*Of the pairs of globes published by Gemma Frisius in about
1536 – 37 in Louvain, only one terrestrial globe and one
celestial globe remain, both in different collections. The pair was
made by the collaboration of three different people who met at the
cradle of globe production in the Netherlands. Gemma Frisius
was responsible for the cartography, Gerard Mercator (1512 –
94), at the beginning of his career as a cartographer, engraved*
*the letters on the copper plates and the remaining engraving was
supplied by Gaspar van der Heyden, who was perhaps also
responsible for the additional construction work. The celestial
globe is a three dimensional copy of the map by Albrecht Dürer
dating from 1515. The nomenclature of the stars and
constellations is more elaborate by comparison with this
example.*

The work of Gemma Frisius and Mercator bears witness to a renaissance of interest in scientific knowledge in which mathematical methods and instruments as well as models were increasingly employed. One of the most influential continental writers in this respect was Petrus Apianus (1495-1552). His *Cosmographicus Liber* (1524), a popular work on geography and astronomy that had many editions, was (re)published by Gemma Frisius (1529). Like Apian, Gemma Frisius wrote about instruments and he is known in particular as the scientist behind the Louvain workshops from which so many high quality scientific instruments such as astrolabes, armillary spheres and globes, have come forth. In particular the terrestrial globe made by Gemma Frisius, in cooperation with Gaspar van der Heyden and Gerard Mercator, is exemplary for the new cartographical knowledge of those days [pl 6 and fig 11]. Yet, as far as globes are concerned the greatest achievement was undeniably made by Gerard Mercator when he produced his terrestrial and celestial globe, in 1541 and 1551 respectively [pls 7 and 8].

Mercator's terrestrial and celestial globes, both with a diameter of 41 cm, were the largest printed globes made up until then. They combined high quality engraving with recent and carefully assessed geographical and astronomical knowledge. Of course, the map of the world as depicted on his terrestrial globe still shows the influence of Ptolemy, such as the excessive size of the Mediterranean, but it also depicts, for the first time correctly, the rhumb lines or loxodromes: the spiral curves on the Earth which outline the path of constant compass direction [fig 12]. His celestial globe still relies on the Ptolemaic star catalogue but it is updated after the latest Copernican theory for precession, published in 1543 [fig 13]. It is no wonder that Mercator's globes were thought to be the best of their times, nor that the standards he set were taken over by other globe makers later in the century. So great was the demand for his globes that orders could not be fulfilled immediately.

fig 12

Sheet with three gores of Mercator's terrestrial globe, 1541

BRUSSELS, KONINKLIJKE BIBLIOTHEEK ALBERT I/BIBLIOTHÈQUE ROYALE ALBERT IER

With his terrestrial globe, Mercator wanted to illustrate his ideas on how the Portuguese discoveries fitted into the Ptolemaic view of Asia. The view of the ancients was that there were three peninsulas in the south of Asia: India, Aurea Chersonesus and Lequii. Further India, the peninsula formed by Indochina, Thailand, Burma and Malaysia, was generally regarded as being the Ptolemaic Aurea Chersonesus. Mercator did not agree with this, since the position of Further India conflicted with Ptolemy's texts. He therefore showed it as a fourth peninsula, between the old ones. Mercator was also able to make terrestrial globes that were suitable for navigation at sea, and for these it was essential that courses could be set. This is almost impossible to do without equipment on the spherical surface of a globe. Mercator therefore added loxodromes to the map. Loxodromes, or lines of the same course, were well known in navigation from their use on 'portulan' charts. A sailor only needed to find the loxodrome that pointed in the right direction towards his destination to know the right compass course to follow, and the chosen course could easily be drawn in using these lines. At least, that was the theory. In practice, the use of globes for navigation at sea was hardly possible.

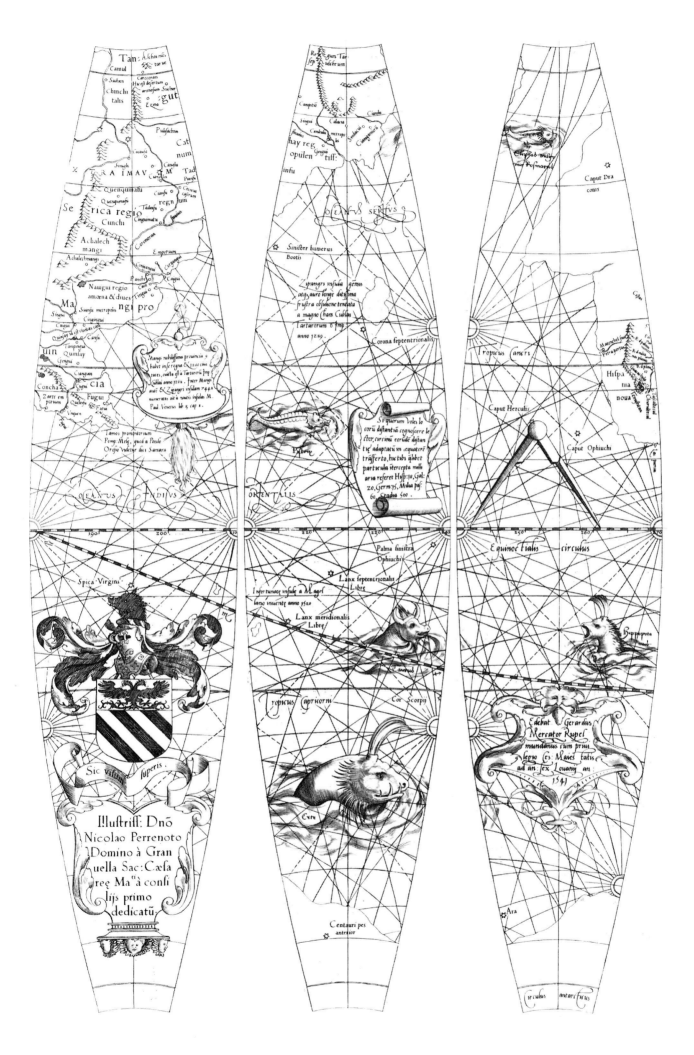

Although a lot of time was saved by printing the cartographic image, the making of a globe was still a job to be carried out carefully. First a perfectly round sphere, a well graduated meridian, an hour circle and a proper stand had to be made. Then the gores had to be pasted with great care on the surface of the sphere and the paper horizon on the horizon ring; thereafter the gores had to be coloured by hand and varnished. Prices depended on the material involved. The Antwerp publisher Plantijn asked 12 guilders for a pair of globes by Gemma Frisius with wooden meridians; 16 guilders 12 stiver for those with brass meridians, whereas for a pair of globes by Gerard Mercator with brass meridians, he demanded 24 guilders. Later, in 1575 the price of a pair of Mercator globes had increased to about 45 guilders.

Compared to the price of a manuscript globe the production of a printed globe was relatively cheap. Yet, throughout the second half of the sixteenth century the demand persisted for expensive luxury manuscript globes, like those made in 1566 by the German mathematician and astronomer Johannes Praetorius (1537–1616) and those ascribed to the workshop of Mercator [fig 14]. In his *La Geographia di Claudio Tolomeo* of 1561 the Italian cartographer Girolamo Ruscelli writes that globes made of copper, bronze or silver were what princes would desire to possess. This may be the reason why Mercato's printed globes hardly met with serious competition. François de Mongenet (*d.* before 1592) and Mario Cartaro (active 1560–91) tried to follow in Mercator's steps but their globes are much smaller. Those of Mongenet did not exceed 8.5 cm, whereas the pair of globes published by Cartaro in 1577 has a diameter of 16 cm and the spheres are made of solid wood.

An exception as far as size is concerned is the terrestrial globe of 71 cm, made between 1564 and 1574 by Giulio and Livio Sanuto (*c.*1520 – 76), two Italian map and globe makers [pl9]. None of these makers made globes in large numbers, as Mercator did. It was only towards the turn of the century, through the globes produced in Amsterdam by Jacob Floris van Langren and his sons Arnold and Hendrik in about 1585 and in London by Emery Molyneux (*d.*1598/99) in 1592, that a new chapter in the history of making printed globes began [fig 15].

fig 13

Sheet with three gores of Mercator's celestial globe, 1551

BRUSSELS, KONINKLIJKE BIBLIOTHEEK ALBERT I/BIBLIOTHÈQUE ROYALE ALBERT IER

For a long time, Mercator's celestial globe was regarded as a work of little importance. It was said that Mercator was a good geographer, but that his astronomical qualities were not of the same calibre. Recent studies have shown that this is not true. On his celestial globe, Mercator set out the stars to the best knowledge of his time. He calculated the positions of the stars for the 1550 epoch, for example, using the recent theory of Copernicus. In addition to the 48 classical constellations, Mercator showed the new constellations Antinous and Coma Berenices probably following the example set by Kaspar Vopel on his celestial globe of 1536. These two 'asterisms' were described in antiquity, but had never been regarded as 'real' constellations. The style of drawing of the constellations with human figures, some naked, others in Roman clothing is also a feature developed by Mercator himself.

Lyra postea Alobore
id est Vultur cadens dicta
χέλυς λύρα

Fidicula
Lyra
Fidinge
Vrna
Brinek

Cepheus
ἰυφεὺς

Via lactea, Lac
γαλαξ

Auis Cygnus
Olor ὄρνις
Adigege

Denct Adiger,
Aridel

Pegasus
Equus Gorgoneus
ἵππος
Alpharaz

Scheat Alp:

Sagitta
Telum ὀϊσός

Delphinus
διλφιν

Equus
ἵππος

Aquila
Vultur Volans
ἀετός Alair

Marrab Alp

Macrab Alp

Emph Alpharaz

Car

Car

Antinous

SAGITTARIVS
Crotus, quabuſdam Chiron
τοξότης

Corona auſtralis
νότιος ςέφανος,
Λίνωτος κυκλος Arato

AQVARIVS
Ganimedes ὑδροχόος

Denct Al-
geth

Vrna
κάλπη

Aqua
ὕδωρ

Scheat
regia Car

Fomahant
Cardano

Piſcis meridionalis
ἰχθὺς νότιος

CAPRICORNVS Pan
ἀιγοκερος, παν Algedi

Louanij anno Domini
1551 menſe Aprili.

fig 14 ▷

The Murad III globes, a pair of globes ascribed to Mercator's workshop
(diameter 11½in/29.5cm, Duisburg, 1579)

PHOTO: CHRISTIE'S IMAGES

This pair of globes must have been a present for the Ottoman Sultan Murad III (1546 – 95). It is not certain whether they ever reached the sultan. They were probably never sent to Turkey, because of the changing political situation, and remained in the possession of some rich noble family for 400 years or so, until they appeared in 1991 for auction. A study of the globes brought to light that they were both modelled after the pair of globes by Mercator. However, the cartography itself had a different source. The positions of the stars on the celestial globe were borrowed from the star catalogue of Johann Schöner, which appeared posthumously in 1551; the cartography of the terrestrial globe is similar to the large map of the world that Mercator had published in 1569. Certain details on the terrestrial globe indicate that it is highly likely that Mercator himself was involved in the production of this pair, which would also be logical. Who else was in such a position to produce globes in 1579?

◁ *fig 15*

Cartouche of the celestial globe by Emery Molyneux
(diameter 24in/61cm, London, 1592)

NUREMBERG, GERMANISCHES NATIONALMUSEUM

The English merchant William Sanderson had a globe made to encourage his countrymen on expeditions to find a sea route via northern passages to China and India. This showed clearly how and where the routes should be sought and what the advantages were. A terrestrial and celestial globe were made at the same time, as was normal. The designer of these was the mathematician and instrument maker Emery Molyneux (d.1598/99). This first English pair of globes shows a clear Dutch influence. The copper plates for both globes were engraved by Jodocus Hondius, in his own characteristic style. In addition, the cartography of the celestial globe is an enlarged copy of that of Jacob Floris van Langren of 1589, which was in turn based on Mercator's globe of 1551 [see pls 7 and 8].

Chapter 3

THE DUTCH REPUBLIC:

Globes for Profit

fig 16

**Large terrestrial globe by Jacob Floris van Langren
(diameter 21in/53.5cm, Amsterdam, 1589)**

AMSTERDAM, RIJKSMUSEUM 'NEDERLANDS SCHEEPVAARTMUSEUM'

*Nothing is known about the training of Jacob Floris van Langren
(d.1610), who produced globes in Amsterdam with his sons
from about 1585. He came from Arnhem and lived for a long
time in the southern Netherlands. It is there that he must have
acquired his knowledge of cartographic techniques and globe
construction. After first making a pair of globes with the modest
diameter of 13in (32.5 cm), this large terrestrial globe followed
in 1589. The basis of the cartography is Mercator's large map of
the world from 1569, with the addition of many new
discoveries. There were plans for the matching celestial globe,
which was to be of the same size, but these were never
implemented.*

In 1654 a new town hall was built in the centre of
Amsterdam. This baroque building, now a Royal
Palace, 'had to express in all its grandeur the essence
of the calling of Amsterdam, the New Rome of the
seventeenth century, a city of peace and prosperity, the
centre of the world – made manifest throughout
architecture, sculpture, painting and wood carving'
(Schöffer, 1975, p.95). Against this background it is
only fitting that the roof of the 'Burgerzaal', at the time
the world's most monumental civic room, where
hundreds of burghers met daily to discuss their affairs,
is symbolically borne by Atlas carrying the celestial
globe. Inlaid in the floor of the room are three grand
planispheres, one showing the northern celestial sky
and the other two the northern and southern
terrestrial hemispheres. Not surprisingly the then most
famous Dutch publisher and producer of globes, Joan
Blaeu (*c.*1599 –1673), the son of Willem Jansz. Blaeu,
was the man behind these planispheres. Joan Blaeu
was one of the magistrates who had to approve of the
building of the town hall. He could afford to spend time
on social affairs. His map and globe industry was by
then one of the most successful and prosperous
enterprises in Amsterdam. Why were Dutch maps and
globes so much in demand?

The Dutch economy had been doing neither very
badly nor extremely well, until after the fall of
Antwerp in 1585 when there came a sudden influx of
capital, intelligence, know-how and enterprise. With
this influx, induced by religious and political strife,

Dutch trade entered a new phase and in its wake the arts and sciences profited greatly. This applied also to map and globe making. The first globe makers who settled in Amsterdam were Jacob Floris van Langren (d.1610) and his sons Arnold (c.1571–1644) and Hendrik (c.1574–1648). Around 1585 they began producing terrestrial [fig16] and celestial globes. Not long after them others, in particular the cartographer and theologian Petrus Plancius (1552–1622), came to Amsterdam. In the early history of Dutch map and globe making the role of Petrus Plancius can not be emphasized enough. In scientific achievement he was the most important cartographer after Mercator, and it was owing to his initiatives in scientific enterprise that Dutch globes ultimately became the most popular in Europe.

The influential role of Petrus Plancius is clearly seen in a series of globes made by a number of Dutch globe makers with whom he cooperated from time to time. The first traces of his activities are manifest in the revised editions of both the terrestrial and celestial globes by Jacob Floris van Langren which appeared in 1589 [fig17]. It was unfortunate for the Van Langrens that their cooperation with Plancius did not last very long. It may well be that conflicting religious opinions interfered with the globe making partnership. Apart from being a cartographer Plancius was also actively engaged as a preacher in Amsterdam. However that may be, the next time we see Plancius involved in globe making it is in cooperation with Jodocus Hondius (1563–1612), who in the course of 1593, after a sojourn in England, had come to set up a workshop in Amsterdam. Hondius was the first globe maker to profit from Plancius's initiative to advance existing knowledge through a particularly ambitious project: a scientific expedition to the southern hemisphere.

Until the 1580s Dutch merchants had restricted their trade to the Baltic and the west coast of Europe. There had been no urgent need to follow the steps taken by the Portuguese and the Spaniards to find a route to China. Merchandise was bought in Lisbon and sold in the northern regions and vice versa, whereby good profits were made. However, when in 1585 for political reasons the Spanish and Portuguese seaports became closed to Dutch merchants, the necessity arose to get the commodities directly from the Far East. Following in the steps of English explorers several voyages were made to find a north-east passage, one of these voyages leading to a spectacular hibernation on Nova Zembla in the winter of 1596–97. However, most Amsterdam merchants, among whom Plancius was the greatest advocate, were in favour of exploiting the Portuguese passage around the Cape of Good Hope. The first voyage along this route departed from Amsterdam in 1595 and Plancius took advantage of it for scientific exploration. The programme he designed consisted of two parts: first to obtain new data on the variation of the magnetic compass, and second to measure the positions of the stars around the south pole, invisible from European latitudes.

fig 17

Southern part of the celestial globe by Van Langren (diameter 13in/32.5cm, Amsterdam, 1589)

LONDON. NATIONAL MARITIME MUSEUM

With the help of Petrus Plancius(1552–1622), Jacob Floris van Langren made a revised edition of his celestial globe of 13in (32.5cm) diameter. On this globe, we see for the first time signs of Plancius's interest in astronomy. He added two new constellations – Crux and Triangulus Antarticus – along with the Magellanic Clouds. He took the positions of the stars in these new constellations, which belonged to the southern part of the sky, from the observations of Andreas Corsali, Amerigo Vespucci and Pedro de Medina, as can be read in a long declaration on the globe.

The results of these scientific explorations, in particular the data on the celestial sky, have considerably affected the production of Dutch globes. Jodocus Hondius was the first globe maker who in cooperation with Plancius produced a series of celestial globes, which showed the newly recorded stars around the south pole, nicely grouped into 12 constellation figures, expressly designed for that purpose by Plancius [fig 18]. The influence of the new data of the variation of the compass on globe making was less direct. Plancius believed that one could find the longitude at sea from such data, an hypothesis that received a lot of opposition among Dutch navigators and other experts in matters of that kind. Map makers and cartographers also differed in opinion over the question of the proper position of the prime meridian. For instance, Jodocus Hondius alternately supported and rejected the opinion of Plancius, and as a result the absolute positions of places on his terrestrial globes are shifted to and fro in the course of time.

By 1600 Hondius had obtained the upper hand in globe making in Amsterdam [pl 10]. His most direct rivals, Jacob van Langren and his sons, were highly capable engravers, but they lacked the scientific background to take full advantage of their position. They tried to secure their interests through a request to obtain the sole rights to make globes in Holland. In direct confrontation with Hondius this battle was lost: there could be no monopoly in globe making for the Van Langrens through the protection of the States General. The decision was fatal for them; because they did not have a scientific adviser of the calibre of Plancius they had no chance in direct competition.

fig 18

Southern sky on the celestial globe of Petrus Plancius, produced by Jodocus Hondius about 1598 (diameter 14 in/35.5 cm, Amsterdam, *c.*1598)

LUCERN, HISTORISCHES MUSEUM; PHOTO: RENÉ VAN DER KROGT

The first Dutch journey to the East was made between 1595 and 1597. During this journey, various observations were made at the request of Petrus Plancius, including observations of the variation of the compass and of the stars in the southern sky that are not visible in our northern latitudes. The stars observed were grouped by Petrus Plancius into twelve new constellations. For these he used mostly the images of animals from the East and West Indies. He made his innovations known by means of this celestial globe engraved by Jodocus Hondius. The new constellation of Phoenix can be seen in the photograph.

fig 19

Three gores of the first celestial globe by Willem Jansz. Blaeu (13½in/34cm, *c.*1598)

CAMBRIDGE, MASS., HARVARD
UNIVERSITY, HOUGHTON LIBRARY

The pioneering astronomical work of Tycho Brahe attracted a number of interested people, including the young Willem Jansz. Blaeu (1571–1638), who visited him in 1595 and spent a winter helping him with his observations. At the same time, he copied Tycho's large celestial globe. On the basis of this, Blaeu made a celestial globe, using the artist Jan Pietersz. Saenredam to draw the figures. The astronomical content combined with the new drawing style made this celestial globe the best and the most modern of its time. Unfortunately, however, it became obsolete almost immediately, since at the same time Plancius and Hondius were finishing their globe, which was the same size and showed the latest celestial discoveries around the south pole.

fig 20

**The Strait of Le Maire on the terrestrial globe
by Willem Jansz. Blaeu
(diameter 13½in/34cm, produced after 1621)**

AMSTERDAM, RIJKSMUSEUM 'NEDERLANDS
SCHEEPVAARTMUSEUM'; PHOTO: RENÉ VAN DER KROGT

*One of the most spectacular discoveries of the first part of the
seventeenth century was the opening of a new sea route south of
America. The Strait of Magellan was thought for almost a
hundred years to be the only western sea route to the East Indies.
Le Maire and Schouten's expedition sailed around Tierra del
Fuego, proving that it was an island, not a part of the great
southern continent of Magallanica, as had been assumed. It was
the only geographical change that Willem Jansz. Blaeu made to
his smaller globes.*

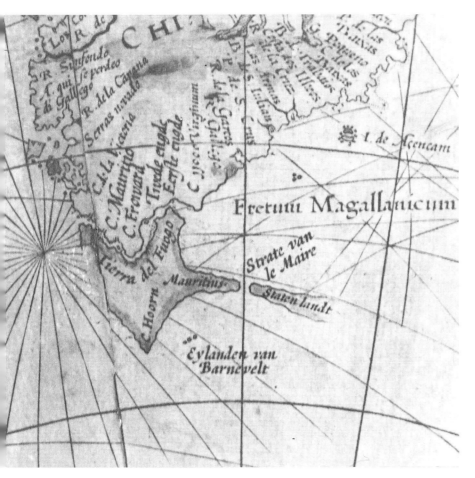

While Hondius and Van Langren were engaged in
their fight about privileges, another globe maker had
entered the scene: a young man from Alkmaar,
Willem Jansz., later known as Willem Jansz. Blaeu
(1571–1638). In the matter of map and globe making
Blaeu was a far more serious opponent for the house of
Hondius than the Van Langrens ever had been, since
Blaeu was quite able to compete with Plancius where
new scientific data were at stake. In order to get the
best data of the positions of the stars for his first
celestial globe, he visited Tycho Brahe (1546–1601),
the leading astronomer of the day and the first in the
Western world after Ptolemy to provide a completely
new star catalogue [fig 19]. Blaeu was not the first
Dutch globe maker to visit Tycho. Arnold and Hendrik
van Langren had preceded him in a trip to Hven, and
they deserve the credit for being the first to have
published Tycho's newly observed star positions on
their celestial globe of 1594. Another call for new data
arose for Blaeu when in 1598 Plancius, in cooperation
with Hondius, published a new celestial globe with
novel data of the stars around the south pole. Blaeu
immediately arranged for a second survey of the
southern celestial sky, to be made by his fellow citizen
of Alkmaar, Frederick de Houtman (c.1570–1627), in
order to circumvent the rights of Plancius on the data
of the first survey. When after some time Blaeu
obtained his new data, he quickly advertised them as
the better, which of course nobody could verify, but
which was easily believed.

After the first voyage more journeys of exploration
were undertaken by the Dutch. Between 1508 and
1601 Olivier van Noort circumnavigated the Earth,
from 1620 Dutch sailors explored the west coast of
Australia and between 1642 and 1644 Abel Tasman
sailed around Australia and discovered New Zealand.
Of particular note is the voyage made between 1615
and 1617 by Willem Cornelisz. Schouten and Jacob Le
Maire. These explorers were commissioned in 1615
by a number of merchants from Amsterdam and
Hoorn (who formed the 'Australische Compagnie', or
Australian Company) to find a new route to the East
in order to circumvent the rights of the Verenigde

fig 21

**Cartouches on the terrestrial globe of
Pieter van den Keere
(diameter 10½ in/26.5 cm, Amsterdam, c. 1612)**

ROTTERDAM, MARITIEM MUSEUM 'PRINS HENDRIK':
PHOTO: RENÉ VAN DER KROGT

*Whilst Hondius and Blaeu were competing against each other
with their globes, Petrus Plancius had a new pair of globes made
in about 1612 by Pieter van den Keere (1571 – after 1646),
the brother-in-law of Jodocus Hondius. The celestial globe served
to make known a number of newly designed constellations, while
the terrestrial globe was used to breathe new life into his ideas on
the connection between the variation of the compass and
geographical longitude. The central cartouche on the terrestrial
globe contains Pieter van den Keere's dedication, and on either
side Plancius sets out his cartographical sources and his theory.*

Oostindische Compagnie (the V.O.C. or Dutch East-India Company), for all trade along the known passages of the Cape of Good Hope and the Strait of Magellan. The discovery of the Strait of Le Maire and the southernmost cape of America, henceforth called after the town Hoorn, Cape Horn, totally changed the then common ideas on the geography of 'Tierra del Fuego' [fig 20]. It was, however, a few years before the Strait of Le Maire could be found on terrestrial globes, in spite of the fact that in 1617 Blaeu had already attempted to include it on his new terrestrial globe of 68 cm. Because of legal hostilities between the Australian Company and the Dutch East-India Company, over the rights to the new route, Blaeu was forbidden to publish this information. When it turned out that the information had been published elsewhere the prohibition was lifted in 1618.

In the first quarter of the seventeenth century competition reigned at all levels in the Dutch economy, the cartographic industry being no exception. The need for globe makers to improve their products in every conceivable way made Dutch maps and globes the best in the world. In the process the scientific and artistic contents of Dutch globes were raised to unprecedented levels. The rival activities of the Van Langrens, the house of Hondius and that of Blaeu resulted in the production of more than twenty new globe editions [figs 21, 22 and 23]. Considering the costs for the engraving of copper plates, not all of these globes were a success commercially. In the end the publishing house of Blaeu came out best and even acquired a monopoly position, not through the protection of some public agency but rather economically through the acquisition of all the precious copper plates of their opponents. As a result Dutch globe making in the second half of the century became a rather dull and routine reproductive process, in no way comparable to the innovative spirit of enterprise that enlivened globe making in Holland during the early part of the seventeenth century.

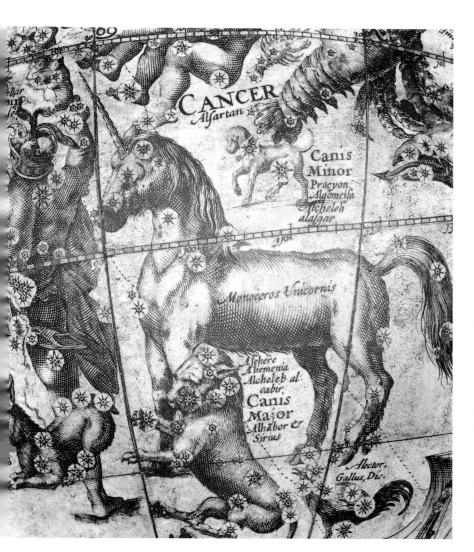

fig 22

The new constellation of Monoceros on the celestial globe by Petrus Plancius and Pieter van den Keere (diameter 10½in/26.5 cm, Amsterdam, *c.*1612)

ROTTERDAM, MARITIEM MUSEUM 'PRINS HENDRIK';
PHOTO: ERIK DE GOEDEREN

Forty-eight constellations had been passed on from the ancients via Ptolemy's Almagest. *It was not until 1536 that two more were added. Kaspar Vopel added a depiction of Coma Berenices and Antinous as constellations on his celestial globe. However, this could hardly be called an expansion, since they were also handed over from antiquity, but had never been officially counted as constellations. The first person really to design new constellations was Petrus Plancius: firstly, 2 on the celestial globe of Van Langren from 1589, followed by another on the celestial maps that were added to his wall map of the world from 1592. After the return of the first Dutch voyage to the East Indies, he grouped the newly described stars into 12 new constellations. In 1612, he was heard of again; 8 new constellations were drawn in gaps between the old ones on the celestial globe that he had had made by Pieter van den Keere. One of these is Monoceros, shown here.*

plate 10

**Terrestrial and celestial globe by Jodocus Hondius
(diameter 14in/35.5 cm, Amsterdam, *c.*1600)**

UTRECHT, ANTIQUARIAAT FORUM

*The first Amsterdam globe by Jodocus Hondius (1563–1612),
the 14-inch terrestrial globe was completed about 1597 and
gave an up-to-date summary of the latest geographical
discoveries. This was primarily the time of the expeditions
searching for the northern passage to China. The globe shows the
results of the English voyages seeking the north-west passage,
and of the first journeys of Willem Barentsz. to the north-east.
The new celestial globe of 1600 showed the latest developments
in charting the southern sky by depicting the new constellations
that Plancius had designed. The globe also follows the new style
of drawing that Jan Pietersz. Saenredam had developed for
Willem Jansz. Blaeu.*

Celestial and terrestrial globe by Willem Jansz. Blaeu (diameter 27in/68cm, *c.*1645/46)

AMSTERDAM, HISTORISCH MUSEUM

The fierce competition between Willem Jansz. Blaeu and Jodocus Hondius moved into a new phase with the completion of Hondius's pair of globes of 21-inch (53.5cm) diameter in 1613. In addition to cartography, size played an important part in this. By 1614, Blaeu was already working on a rival work – a pair of globes of such a size that had never been seen in Amsterdam. In 1616, the celestial globe was finished, followed by the terrestrial globe the next year. The large, costly pair of globes was a huge success. Various new editions followed, with modifications to the cartography of the terrestrial globe. The last changes were made by Willem's son, Joan Blaeu, just after 1645. All the discoveries relating to New Holland (Australia) and New Zealand, including those made by Abel Jansz. Tasman, were added, with the result that some of the beautiful cartouches disappeared. The owners of these majestic globes regarded them as extremely valuable possessions, and the fact that there are today at least 200 of these terrestrial and celestial globes in various collections can be seen as proof of this.

fig 23 ▷

**Dedication cartouche from the terrestrial globe of
Jodocus Hondius, Jr and Adriaen Veen
(diameter 21in/53.5cm, Amsterdam, 1613)**

AMSTERDAM, RIJKSMUSEUM 'NEDERLANDS
SCHEEPVAARTMUSEUM'; PHOTO: RENÉ VAN DER KROGT

*Around 1611, Jodocus Hondius, Sr started on the production of
a pair of 21-inch globes, but work on them was halted by his
death in February 1612. With the help of the navigational
expert Adriaen Veen (b.1572), Hondius, Jr (1593–1629)
completed the pair, and in June 1613, they presented the globes
to the States General. A richly decorated cartouche on the
terrestrial globe contains the dedication. The text is surrounded
by female figures, representing fortitude, inspiration, arithmetic
and geometry. Navigational instruments are 'hanging' on the
left, with surveying instruments on the right.*

◁ *plate 13*
A group of Gerard and Leonard Valk globe pairs

UTRECHT, UNIVERSITEITSMUSEUM; PHOTO: ERIK DE GOEDEREN

*The first quarter of the eighteenth century saw a revival in globe
production in Amsterdam. Gerard Valk (1652–1726),
working later with his son Leonard (1675–1746), produced
seven different globe pairs with diameters in a regular series
3 inches apart: 3, 6, 9, 12, 15, 18 and 24in (7.75, 15, 23,
31, 39, 46 and 62cm). Both the terrestrial and celestial globes
by Valk are characterized by their modern cartography.
However, they were only known in the Republic of the United
Netherlands, where there was almost a monopoly. The
photograph shows the collection of Valk's globes in the
Universiteitsmuseum in Utrecht: the 3-inch pocket globe, a
tellurium with a 3-inch terrestrial globe, a pair of 12-inch globes
and the largest celestial globe. Both globes of the 12-inch pair
are placed with the south pole upwards in the frame, so that the
southern constellations and the Australian discoveries
can be seen.*

The competitive development of the Dutch globe making industry described here was coupled with an ever increasing demand for maps and globes. In the early decades of the seventeenth century the use of globes aboard ships for navigational purposes was advocated by the Dutch East-India Company. Whether or not these globes served indeed as an aid in navigation is a matter for debate, but there is every reason to believe that globes were intensively used in educating navigators, both at home and at sea. The production of globes went hand in hand with the publication of treatises for their use, all of which are said to be of interest to students of astronomy and geography, but most of all to the advantage of navigators. In all these books the globe, whether celestial or terrestrial, is appraised as an easy aid in mastering common navigational problems. Later in the seventeenth century when the success of the Dutch commercial enterprises made itself felt at all levels of society, the interest in globes came in particular from merchants and burghers who aspired to an intellectual image. The production of Blaeu's large pair of globes of 68 cm diameter, a luxury edition for the very rich, aimed to provide for the demands of this new market [pls 11 and 12].

The fame of Dutch globes spread quickly, and soon these globes were found everywhere in Europe. The large pair of globes of 68 cm by Blaeu is even nowadays frequently encountered adorning libraries and palaces in Italy and other European countries. The success of Dutch globes is also clear from the many imitations by foreign makers, among whom the Italians Matthäus Greuter and Giuseppe de Rossi (see chapter 4) and the Frenchman Jean Boisseau (see chapter 5) are the most notable. By the end of the century the existing cartographic tradition had been taken over by Jan Jansz. van Ceulen (1635 – 89) [fig 24]. In 1682 he bought all the copper plates and tools for making globes from the heirs of Joan Blaeu. He succeeded in protecting his investment by a privilege from the States of Holland and West-Friesland for the sole right to publish globes in Holland. It is not clear to what extent this patent prevented the sales of foreign globes,

as for instance those of Coronelli, in Holland. Of more importance was the rise in Amsterdam of the new globe firm of Gerard Valk (1652 –1726), later taken over by his son Leonard (1675 –1746). Gerard Valk, who in 1680 had founded a publishing firm for maps and atlases together with Petrus Schenk (c.1661–1711), started with the production of globes at the turn of the century, as an enterprise of his own. He did not rely on the existing copper plates of the old school but designed a totally new pair of globes,

fig 24
Pocket globe by Abraham van Ceulen (diameter 2 in/5 cm, Amsterdam, 1697)

LONDON. TREVOR PHILIP & SONS LTD

'From Abraham van Ceulen, Art and map colourist in Amsterdam on Singel by Jan-Roonpoorts tower, in the house 'Atlas', very curious small terrestrial globes may be obtained for a reasonable price. (They are) two inches in diameter, enclosed in leather cases in which the celestial globe is applied to the lining; each (is) perfectly illuminated according to its type. All lovers of astronomy and other arts (will find it) very easy to carry with them, just like a pocket watch.' (advertisement in the Amsterdamsche Courant, 20 April 1697). An example of this small pocket globe was found as late as 1990. The celestial globe is a reduction of Blaeu's 13.5-centimetre globe of 1606. The cartography is geocentric. This can be clearly seen if we compare the photo with Joseph Moxon's (see pl 31) and then look at Ursa Major; in Moxon's, it points to the left, in Van Ceulen's to the right. The terrestrial globe features early seventeenth-century cartography and is based on a small terrestrial globe that is ascribed to Blaeu.

based on the latest geographical and astronomical information [fig 25]. Around 1700 the latest geographical data came from Paris, as will be explained in Chapter 5, whereas the most recent data on the stars and their constellations had been observed by the Polish astronomer Johannes Hevelius (1611–87) in Danzig (Gdansk). In 1687 he published a new star atlas *Firmamentum Sobiescianum sive Uranographia*, and in 1690 his star catalogue *Prodomus Astronomiae*, was published posthumously. Hevelius was the last of the astronomers who did not use a

telescope to measure the positions of the stars. He had very good eye sight and argued that his measurements were no worse than those obtained with the telescopes of the day, which were optically not very reliable. Hevelius's star positions and his newly designed constellations are encountered on most celestial globes made in the first half of the eighteenth century [fig 26]. This is not surprising: the star maps in Hevelius's atlas were expressly designed in globe view and could therefore directly be copied by globe makers.

The new Amsterdam globes, produced in seven different sizes inclusive of a pocket globe, were mainly sold to the local Dutch market [pl 13]. Gerard Valk died in 1726, and the business was continued first by Leonard, and later by his widow [fig 27]. It appears that the son was doing less well than his father: maybe due to the absence of an international outlet. The situation improved later in the century when the globe factory was taken over by Petrus Schenk, Jr

(1728 –1803), a nephew of Leonard's wife. At the turn of the century the latter sold the business to the Amsterdam publishing house Covens & Mortier. For a short while the globe making industry revived again in Holland. Cornelis Covens (1764 –1825), who designed a new terrestrial globe, brought the constellation figures on the existing celestial globes up to date. However, with the death of Covens in 1825 the production of globes in the Netherlands came to an end.

fig 25

Northern America on Valk's terrestrial globe (diameter 18 in/46 cm, Amsterdam, 1715)

ROTTERDAM, MARITIEM MUSEUM 'PRINS HENDRIK': PHOTO: RENÉ VAN DER KROGT

The cartography of Valk's globes is characterized by a wealth of detail and the complete absence of decorative elements. Even the cartouches are surrounded by a simple edge of leaves. The map itself is based on the best sources, mainly French. Hypothetical coastlines are not shown, or are shown with a faint line, as can be seen in the north-west of America. Until the eighteenth century, it was regarded as an undisputed fact that the peninsula of California was an island, as shown in the photograph.

fig 26

The constellation 'Lynx' on Valk's celestial globe (24 in/62 cm, Amsterdam, 1728)

UTRECHT, UNIVERSITEITSMUSEUM; PHOTO: ERIK DE GOEDEREN

Gerard Valk used the latest astronomical information for his celestial globes. The constellations and the style in which the figures were drawn were copied by Valk from the atlas shortly to be known as Uranographia (1687) by Johannes Hevelius

(1611– 87). However, Valk conscientiously acknowledged his source: not only did he entitle his globes Uranographia, but he also gave Hevelius as the author. One of the nine constellations that were introduced by Hevelius is Lynx, a constellation which included a number of weak stars between Ursa Major and Auriga. One has to have very sharp eyes to be able to observe these stars, and Hevelius therefore named the constellation after an animal that is well-known for its sharp eyes – the lynx.

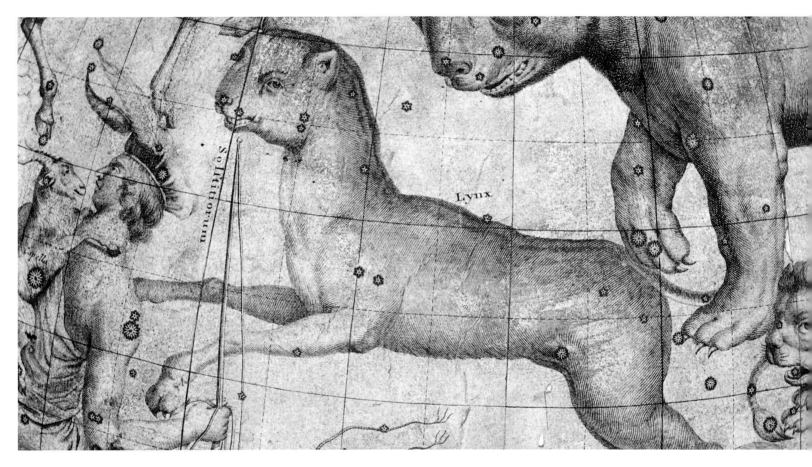

fig 27 ▷

The date on Valk's 12-inch terrestrial globe changed by pasting in a '5' in the year

AMSTERDAM, RIJKSMUSEUM 'NEDERLANDS SCHEEPVAARTMUSEUM'; PHOTO: RENÉ VAN DER KROGT

After Leonard Valk died childless in 1746, his widow Maria Schenk continued making globes, probably in collaboration with her brother Petrus Schenk II (1693 –1775). They 'renewed' the globes by changing the date to 1750. They obviously had a large number of sheets that had already been printed. The change in the date was made by sticking the figure '5' or the figures '50', which were printed on a separate piece of paper, in the right position on the date.

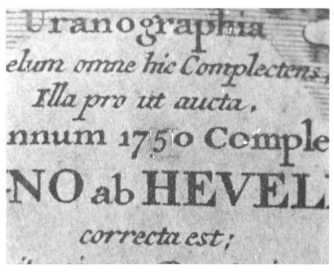

Chapter 4

ITALY:

A Fancy
for Decoration

**Part of a decorative frame, made by an unknown
artist for a pair of Vincenzo Coronelli globes of
42in/110cm diameter (globe: Venice, 1693)**

*The Italian globe maker Vincenzo Coronelli (1650–1718)
made his name primarily in Italy and Central Europe. Never
equalled, his largest pair of globes, with diameters of 43 inches
(110cm), are still highly prized pieces in a large number of
libraries. For a showpiece such as this, the normal frame
supplied by Coronelli was often not splendid enough. The library
would look for an artist who could make a frame worthy of such
a great work of art. It is only rarely known who the artist is, and
this is the case with the frame for the Coronelli pair in the
Musées Royaux d'Art et d'Histoire in Brussels. Both the
terrestrial and the celestial globes are mounted in frames that are
richly decorated with wood carvings. On each globe, the four
supports for the horizon are formed from the torsos of allegorical
human figures. On the terrestrial globe, they represent the
continents of Europe, Africa, Asia and America, and on the
celestial globe, the four elements – earth, water, air and fire
[see also figs 30 and 31].*

In the last quarter of the seventeenth century the
Dutch globe making industry had outlived itself
scientifically as well as artistically. In this and the
following chapters we shall see how the vacuum
that thus arose in European globe making was filled.
In the present chapter we turn our attention to Italy
where until the middle of the sixteenth century the
map making industry had flourished as nowhere else,
as is illustrated by the repute of map makers like
Giacomo Gastaldi, Paolo Forlani and Antonio Lafreri.
Despite this the globe making industry did not follow
suit, with the exception of the work of the Sanuto
brothers (see chapter 2). As has been remarked by
Edward L. Stevenson in his *Terrestrial and Celestial
Globes* (1921) there appears to have been in Italy a
definite preference for making manuscript globes over
printed globes. The luxurious taste, the appeal to status
which a spectacular and preferably large sized globe
has, and a general fancy for decoration are elements
that may have been of influence [fig 28]. Manuscript
globes of all sizes were made from the sixteenth until
the beginning of the eighteenth century. Carlo Benci
(1616–76) and Amanzio Moroncelli (1652–1719),
both of whom were Sylvestrian monks, made globes
with diameters varying from 1 to 2 metres. Globe
making was seemingly very popular among the
Italian members of conventual orders: the most
famous of all Italian globe makers, Vincenzo Coronelli

(1650 –1718), who started his career by making manuscript globes, also belonged to a religious order. However, before turning to him, we first shall discuss some printed globes made in Italy in the first half of the seventeenth century by Matthäus Greuter (1556 –1638) and Giuseppe de Rossi (first quarter of the seventeenth century). Matthäus Greuter was born in Strassburg, where he learned to engrave copper. He moved around in France until he settled in Rome at the beginning of the seventeenth century. There he produced a large plan of Rome, *Disegno nuovo di Roma* (1618) and a large map of Italy (1620 or 1630). In the 1630s he subsequently produced two pairs of globes of 26.5 and 49 cm diameter, respectively. For the cartographic image of his terrestrial globes he relied strongly on that of the 68 cm terrestrial globe published by Willem Blaeu (pls 11 and 12); the image of his celestial globes was copied from those published by Pieter van den Keere and Petrus Plancius (figs 21 and 22). After his death in 1638 several editions of his globes appeared; some have the impression 'Da Stampa da Gio Batta de Rossi Milanese in Piazza Nauona Roma'.

fig 29

Terrestrial globe by Matthäus Greuter (diameter 19½in/49 cm, Rome, 1632; republished by 'R.C.A.', Rome, 1744)

ROTTERDAM, MARITIEM MUSEUM 'PRINS HENDRIK':
PHOTO: RENÉ VAN DER KROGT

The globes that Matthäus Greuter (1566 –1638) produced in Rome in 1632 are successors to the 26-inch pair of globes by Willem Jansz. Blaeu dating from 1622. Apart from the smaller size, Greuter made other changes – the loxodromes are not included in the seas, for example. Greuter's globes were issued again without change in the second half of the seventeenth century by Giovanni Battista de Rossi (fl.1640 –72). A completely modified version of the large terrestrial globe is known from 1744, signed 'In Roma nella calcografia della R.C.A. al Pie di Marmo'.

plate 14

Terrestrial and celestial globes by Giuseppe de Rossi (diameter 8in/20cm, Rome, 1615)

In 1615 in Rome, Giuseppe de Rossi produced a very accurate copy of the globes made by Jodocus Hondius in Amsterdam in 1601. The only changes are the dedication and the date. On Hondius's globe the year 1600 appears as the epoch next to the date of issue. De Rossi showed his ignorance by changing both the year of issue and the epoch to 1615 and 1614 respectively, maintaining the difference of one year. De Rossi seems to have had more success with his globes than Hondius – Hondius's original is extremely rare nowadays, while De Rossi's copy appears regularly.

Giovanni Battista de Rossi (active 1640 – 72) was a member of a family enterprise, that among other things was occupied with the reproduction of globes. Already in 1615 another member of this family, Giuseppe de Rossi, had republished the small 20 cm globes, first produced by Jodocus Hondius in 1601 [pl 14]. The publishing house of De Rossi remained active for a long time. Another edition of Greuter's globes appeared in 1695 with the impression 'Roma ex Calcographie Domoci De Rubeis' (De Rossi). Much later the copper plates apparently came into the hands of another firm, R.C.A. in Rome which used them again in 1744 [fig 29]. The members of the De Rossi firm

plate 15
Some globes by Charles-François Delamarche.
Celestial globe of 7 in (18 cm), dated 1770, armillary
sphere with small terrestrial globe, 1780,
and a terrestrial globe of 9½ in/24 cm diameter, 1787

VIENNA, PRIVATE COLLECTION

The first person to direct the production of globes in France at the general public, and to succeed in this, was Charles-François Delamarche (1740 –1817). Delamarche's workshop was in the 'Rue du Foin St. Jacques au Collège Me. Gervais' in the Quartier Latin, the centre of the book trade in Paris, although in 1805 he moved to the Rue du Jardinet. Globes were produced with diameters of 7, 9½, 13 and 25 inches (18, 24, 32.5 and 63.5 cm). For use in armillary spheres, a special small terrestrial globe was made, measuring about 2 inches (5.5 cm). In order to keep his globes and spheres as cheap as possible, he abandoned the expensive brass rings; instead, the meridian of the globe and the rings of the spheres were made, like the horizons, in wood or stiff board. The degrees are printed on paper and stuck on. A characteristic of Delamarche is that the narrow outer side of these rings is painted red.

introduced no new products: their activity was a predominantly reproductive sequel to the Dutch tradition of globe making. Only at the turn of the century, with the emergence of Vincenzo Coronelli, was a truly Italian printed globe designed and successfully produced, with all the adornments such a globe demanded.

Vincenzo Coronelli was the first globe maker of international repute after the hegemony of the Dutch, a phenomenon that had not gone unnoticed in the Netherlands. In 1688 the Leiden professor Isaac Vossius wrote to a friend: 'There is a Venetian monk in Paris who makes very handsome globes out of wood, measuring three feet in diameter and this at a reasonable price, the pair for sixteen pistols. However, the proportions of the lands and the seas do not correspond at all to the true size' (Van der Krogt, 1993, p. 301). The Venetian monk here referred to was, of course, Vincenzo Coronelli, but what was this Italian member of the Franciscan order doing in Paris, and were his globes indeed as bad as Vossius suggests?

Vincenzo Coronelli was born in Venice in 1650. He is said to have been apprenticed in the art of wood cutting. At the age of fifteen he became a novice to the Franciscan order of Conventual Friars Minor, and in 1671 he entered the convent of S. Maria Gloriosa dei Frari in Venice. It was here, in this convent in 1686, that Coronelli set up a workshop for the production of globes. By that time he had already achieved international recognition.

The first pair of manuscript globes made by Coronelli were to adorn the library of the Duke Ranuccio Farnese of Parma. It was a stroke of luck that this pair was seen by the Ambassador of the French King in the court of Rome, Cardinal César d'Estrées, because Coronelli then received the important commission to make a pair of globes for the French King Louis XIV, now known as the Marly globes. It was for their production that Coronelli stayed in Paris from 1681 until 1683. The grandeur of these globes, which were finished in 1683 and which have a diameter of 3.85 metres, made him the globe maker par excellence to the nobility in Europe.

It was only after this event that Coronelli seriously considered taking up the production of maps and globes. Yet, the production of his first printed globes had to wait until 1688 for a number of reasons. First of all Coronelli had to organize the capital needed for his publishing enterprise. This he achieved in a remarkable way: in 1684 he founded the Accademia Cosmografica degli Argonauti. Members of the society, among whom one finds cardinals, archbishops, ambassadors and scientists, were expected to subscribe to the works produced by Coronelli. In order to cover a wide European market, local divisions were set up in other countries, by which the collection of money and the distribution of the printed works and the globes was organized. The other problem Coronelli had to cope with was the lack of qualified engravers in Venice: the craft, which in the days of Gastaldi had set the fashion in Europe, had declined since. This is why, for the production of his first pair of printed globes of 3-foot diameter, Coronelli sought the cooperation of the French engraver to the King, Jean Baptiste Nolin (1657–1725) [figs 30 and 31]. The latter was to engrave the celestial globe in Paris, after drawings provided by Coronelli. The terrestrial globe was engraved in Coronelli's workshop where he had attracted a number of skilled engravers from Italy and from abroad. In the decade following the first edition of the 3-foot terrestrial and celestial globes, various editions of globes of different sizes followed, most of which were made in Venice [fig 32].

Another remarkable aspect of Coronelli's entrepreneurial capacities was his marketing. In order to demonstrate the excellence of his globes he published an atlas *Libro dei Globi*, which included the printed gores of all the pairs of globes he had published, so that everyone could easily verify the superiority of his globes. The complete history of the various changes introduced by Coronelli in the subsequent editions of his printed globes, celestial as well as terrestrial, still

has to be sorted out. It is therefore not yet possible to confirm Coronelli's claim on superiority or to verify the criticism of Vossius. As Helen Wallis, in her introduction to the facsimile of the copy in the British Museum of the *Libro dei Globi*, remarked on his 3-foot terrestrial globe: 'As a record of knowledge in 1688 it was remarkably authoritative. By 1707 it could hardly claim still to be the most perfect of its day' (Wallis, 1969, p.XIII). Indeed, between 1688 and 1707, the activities of French geographers had reformed cartography. Similarly, by 1707 Coronelli's celestial globe seems to have become outdated through the publication of the star catalogue of Hevelius in 1690. On the other hand, Coronelli's 'concave globe gores' were an interesting variation on the common celestial ones. As noticed before (see chapter 1), the common 'convex' celestial globe shows the 'concave' celestial sky as it appears to an observer outside the celestial sphere. This makes the common celestial globe rather unfit for practical use, a shortcoming

figs 30 and 31
Pair of Coronelli's largest globes (diameter 43in/110cm, Paris, 1688)

BRUSSELS, KONINKLIJKE MUSEA VOOR KUNST EN GESCHIEDENIS/ MUSÉES ROYAUX D'ART ET D'HISTOIRE; PHOTO: KONINKLIJK INSTITUUT VOOR HET KUNSTPATRIMONIUM/ INSTITUT ROYAL DU PATRIMOINE ARTISTIQUE

The largest printed globes by Coronelli were also the first that he gave to be printed. The first edition of these appeared in 1688 as a reduced, printed version of the globes that he had made for Louis XIV. In order to ensure guaranteed sales, the globes were available by subscription beforehand. Encouraged by his success Coronelli strove to be independent of the Parisian engraver, Jean-Baptiste Nolin, who had in 1688 engraved the gores of the celestial globe. In 1692 to 1693, Coronelli had Alessandro dalla Via in Venice engrave three new sets of gores for the large globes, i.e. one terrestrial and two celestial globes, in a convex and concave design respectively. Jean-Baptiste Nolin in Paris also engraved a new celestial globe in 1603 after a design by Arnold Deuvez, which he dedicated to Coronelli.

highlighted by Carlo Malavista in a lecture given in 1692 at the Accademia Fisico-Matematica in Rome. 'To make it easier to understand, the illustrious Giovanni Ciampini, Director of the Academy, has thought fit to have the celestial globe of Coronelli divided into two halves in concave form, so that the stars are seen in their proper location, agreeing with the way we look at them in the sky, without the person having to fatigue his mind in observing them by imagining that he is standing in the centre of the ball' (Wallis, 1969, p.IX). However, the existing convex gores were of course unsuitable for a concave globe. To provide for this need Coronelli designed his

'concave' gores which had to be pasted on the inside of a sphere. Yet, no properly mounted copy of his concave globe is known: the concave gores appear to have been pasted on the outside of spheres!

The publication of his *Libro dei Globi* in 1697 is a landmark in the history of globe making and it is to be deplored that after Coronelli's death no one in the convent where he worked till his death could continue his work. The precious plates were sold at the price of the copper and this was the end of an enterprise that had dominated the globe making industry in Europe for about thirty years.

In Italy globe making seems to have ceased entirely after Coronelli's death. As mentioned above, some of the early and truly outdated globes by Greuter were published again in 1744 by the 'Calcographia della RCA' in Rome. In the same period (1754) Gianfranco Costa (*d.*1773) produced a celestial globe of 20 cm diameter. A small number of manuscript terrestrial globes (diameters 150 cm) by Pietro Rosini (active 1762), an Olivetan monk, are preserved, but very little is known about this maker. Towards the end of the eighteenth century, a lay brother of the 'Ordine dei Clerici regolari Somaschi' (CRS), Giovanni Maria Cassini (*c.*1745 – 1824/30), produced a pair of globes in Rome [fig 33]. Cassini was an important engraver, known in particular for his landscapes and architectural views. His most impressive cartographical work is the *Nuovo Atlante geografico universale*, which was published in Rome in three volumes between 1792 and 1801. Cassini's globes seem to have served a local market. It is unknown how extensive his production was.

fig 32 ▷

Gores of Coronelli's smallest globes (diameter 2 in/5 cm, Venice, 1697)

LEIDEN, UNIVERSITEITSBIBLIOTHEEK

Coronelli's small globes are also the rarest. Gores of the 4-inch and 2-inch (10 cm and 5 cm) pairs were published in his Libro dei Globi (1697). Hardly any mounted examples of these globes are known to be in existence, and it is possible that they were not available as mounted globes. The sheet with the gores of the smallest pair, which are handsomely placed in a cartouche, appears in various Coronelli atlases.

◁ *fig 33*

Gores of the celestial globe by Giovanni Maria Cassini (diameter 13 in/33 cm, Rome, 1792)

BERLIN, STAATSBIBLIOTHEK

The first part of the three-part Nuovo Atlante geografico universale *(Rome, 1792 –1801) by the Roman engraver Giovanni Maria Cassini (c.1745 –1824/30) includes the gores for a terrestrial and a celestial globe. Mounted examples of these globes are primarily to be found in Italian collections. In the cartouche of the celestial globe, it is stated that the catalogues of Flamsteed and Lacaille were used as sources. The design of Cassini's globes is much less sophisticated than the globes that were made at the same time in London and Paris.*

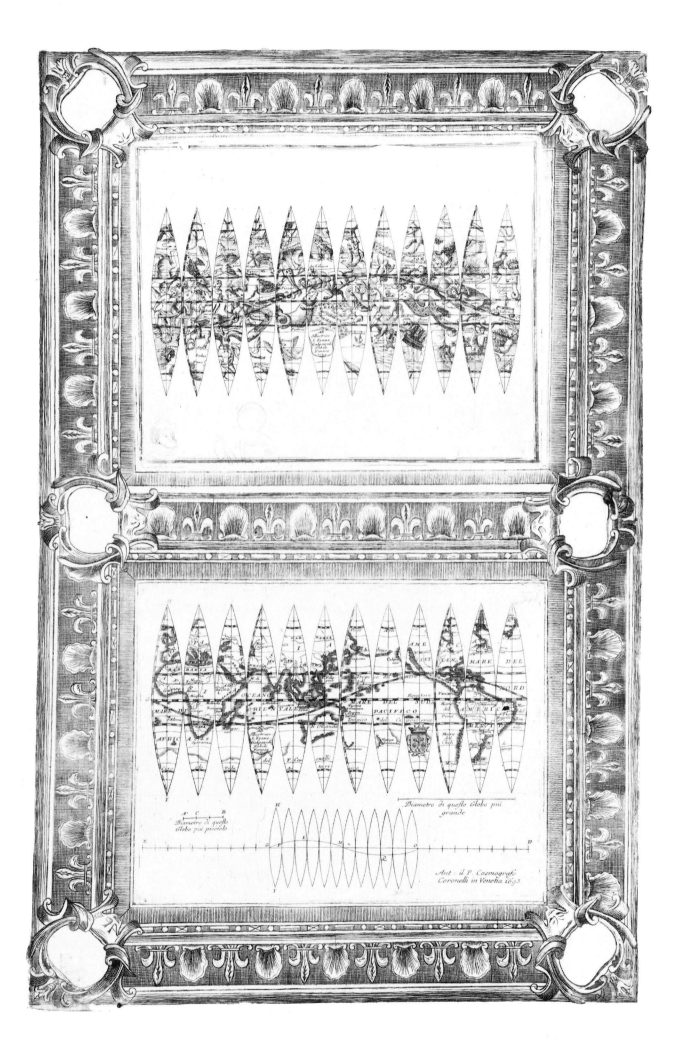

ATLAS FRANÇOIS,
CONTENANT LES CARTES GEOGRAPHIQUES
dans lesquelles sont tres exactement remarquez
LES EMPIRES, MONARCHIES,
ROYAUMES et ESTATS
DE L'EUROPE, DE L'ASIE, DE L'AFRIQUE
ET DE L'AMÉRIQUE :
AVEC LES TABLES ET CARTES PARTICULIERES,
DE FRANCE, DE FLANDRE, D'ALLEMAGNE
D'ESPAGNE ET D'ITALIE.
DEDIÉ AU ROY,
Par son tres-humble, tres-obeissant, tres-fidele Sujet et Serviteur
HUBERT JAILLOT Geographe ordinaire de sa Majesté.

Chapter 5

FRANCE:

Globes made by the 'Géographes du Roi'

fig 34

Globe in an allegorical representation.
Frontispiece of the *Atlas François* by Hubert Jaillot

The French globe of the world is carried on the shoulders of Atlas and Hercules (with the lionskin). The globe features three fleur-de-lys and a faint map of the world, on which the coast of France can be seen. The globe is crowned with the laurel wreath of Victory, Fame proclaims its renown. This is the central representation on the frontispiece of the Atlas François *published by the Parisian publisher Hubert Jaillot (1632 –1712) in about 1692. The globe is used here as a symbol of the world and the French supremacy over it. At the bottom right, the conquered peoples pay tribute. Half hidden behind the sail bearing the title, we see a second globe with a telescope and an atlas – the symbols of French navigation.*

In 1666 L'Académie Royale des Sciences was founded in Paris under the protection of Louis XIV. From the start the French Academy took a lively interest in geographical sciences and through its efforts Paris became the most important cartographical centre of the eighteenth century [fig 34]. Accurate scientific mapping based on exact astronomical observations, in particular of geographical longitudes, for a variety of reasons became possible for the first time in the second half of the seventeenth century. Through the invention of the telescope four satellites of the planet Jupiter had been discovered by Galilei Galileo in 1608 which because of their short rotation periods were much more suitable for longitude determination than our own Moon. The availability of well regulated pendulum clocks as invented in 1657 by Christiaan Huygens, who was one of the foreign members of the Academy attracted by Colbert in order to enhance its prestige, was another prerequisite for precise observation.

One of the central figures in the geographic research programme of the Academy was Gian Domenico Cassini (Cassini I, 1625 –1712), the director of the newly founded observatory in Paris, who in 1666 had tabulated the eclipses of the satellites of Jupiter. Worldwide expeditions were undertaken and astronomical observations were made in stations as far apart as Quebec, the Cape of Good Hope and Peking. Thus at last the precise extent of the length of the Mediterranean, which had been estimated too large since Ptolemy, could be established. The new geographical data became public in 1696 through the world map drawn by Cassini's son, Jacques (Cassini II, 1677–1756) and engraved by Jean Baptiste Nolin, Sr (1651–1725). The French cartographic programme continued far into the eighteenth century. All sorts of scientific expeditions were undertaken: to China, where Jesuit scientists explored the country geographically, to Peru (1735 – 38) and to Lapland (1736 – 37), in order to settle the well-known debate on the flattening of the Earth.

During the seventeenth century only a few printed globes had been published in France, mostly in imitation of the then famous Dutch globes [fig 35]. This situation changed at the turn of the century when through the French cartographic programme interest in map and globe making increased considerably. A most noteworthy scientist to profit from the newly obtained data was Guillaume Delisle (1675 –1726), a pupil of Gian Domenico Cassini. In 1702 Delisle became a member of the French Academy of Sciences and in 1718 he received the title 'Premier Géographe du Roi'. Among the several works he produced is a terrestrial and celestial globe with a diameter of 31cm [figs 36 and 37]. It established the scientific status of the French globe, but as Monique Pelletier has argued, there still lacked an industry which produced globes for the domestic market. Nevertheless, in the first half of the eighteenth century several globes were manufactured by so-called 'fondeurs'. A 'fondeur' was an instrument maker, belonging to a particular corporation. At least four 'fondeurs', Nicolas Bion (1652 –1733) [fig 38], Jean-Baptiste Delure (d.1736) [fig 39], Jacques-Nicolas Baradelle (1701– after 1770?) and Louis-Charles Desnos (1725 – 91?), are known to have made globes.

fig 35

**Gores for a celestial globe by Jean Boisseau
(diameter 5½in/14cm, Paris, *c.*1640)**

PARIS, BIBLIOTHÈQUE NATIONALE

*The Parisian map colourist and publisher Jean Boisseau (active
1631– 48) copied the pair of 5¹⁄₂in (14 cm) diameter globes by
Pieter van den Keere dating from 1614. These globes show the
eight new constellations that Plancius had formed in the 'open
spaces' between the Ptolemaic constellations. A distinctive
feature is the Jordan, Euphrates and Tigris 'rivers' which 'flow'
between the constellations on the northern hemisphere.*

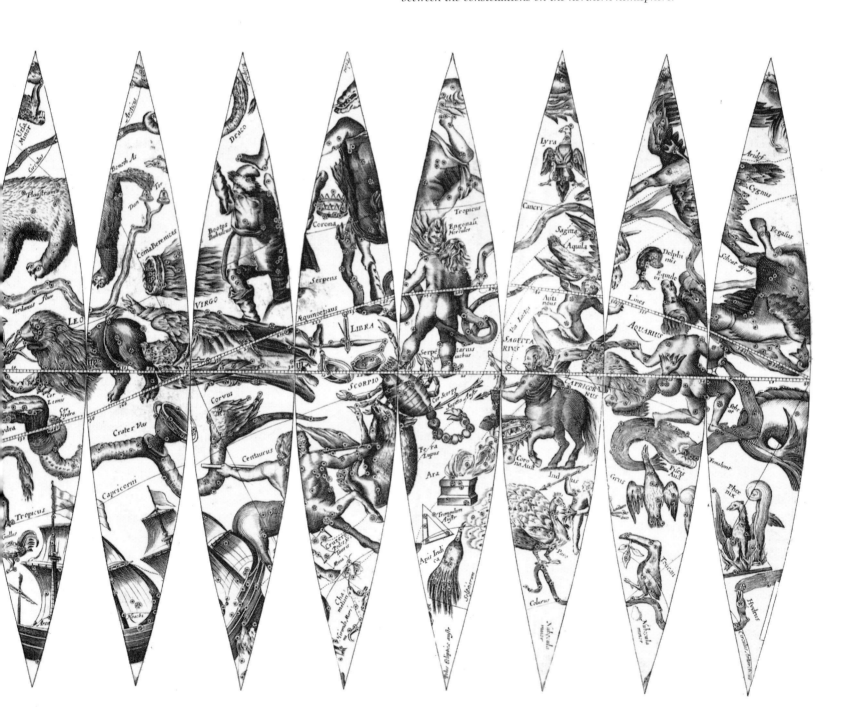

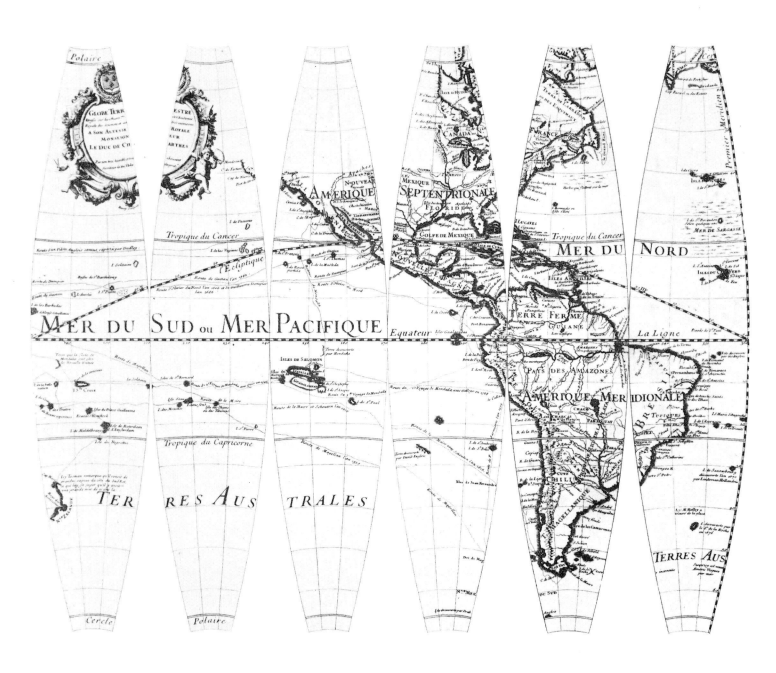

figs 36 and 37

Gores of the terrestrial globe by Guillaume Delisle (diameter 12in/31cm, Paris, 1700)

VINCENNES, SERVICE HISTORIQUE DE LA MARINE

The most important French cartographer from the beginning of the eighteenth century was Guillaume Delisle (1675–1726). Under the supervision of the Académie des Sciences, he drew the positions of places and outlines of continents in line with the latest scientific developments. He finally removed for good errors that could be traced back to Ptolemy's Geography, such as the excessive length of the Mediterranean Sea. Delisle stripped his maps of any elements that were rooted solely in fantasy. He was also the first to be brave enough to leave 'blanks' in areas that had not yet been explored, thus laying the basis for an entire review of cartography.

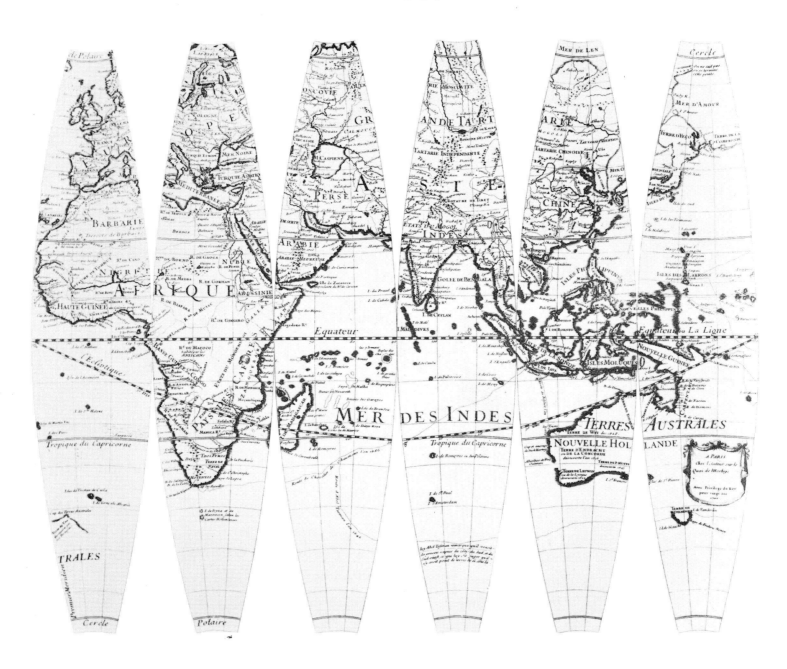

Desnos entered the globe business through a marriage with the widow of Nicolas Hardy (before 1717 – 44), who with his father had set up a business in 1738. Later Desnos exchanged the title 'fondeur' for the more prestigious and profitable ones of 'ingenieur géographe' and 'marchand libraire'.

None of the four globe makers mentioned seems to have been very productive. One reason may be because of the social structures in which they had to operate: 'fondeurs' did not have the right to engrave. To produce a new edition of a globe meant having to find an engraver willing to produce the gores. For instance, the gores of Baradelle were engraved by Claude Roy, and Desnos is known to have cooperated with Jean-Baptiste Nolin, the geographer. According to Monique Pelletier another reason was that the production was delayed through pure lack of skill in globe construction: 'They did not really know how to construct globes with accuracy and with a kind of cleanness without which accuracy is useless... all was spoiled by construction process.' (Pelletier, 1987, p.132) This situation reveals a common feature of instrument making, where the use of an instrument is often quite well publicized but the practical details of their construction remained a secret, no doubt for protective reasons. Books on the use of globes throughout the centuries are manifold, but books on their construction are relatively rare. In 1699 Nicolas Bion published his *L'usage des globes célestes et terrestres et des sphères,* . . . which indeed did contain instruction for the making of globes although it lacked practical details. It was only in 1757 through the excellent article 'Globes' on the precise construction of globes, published in Diderot's *L'Encyclopédie* and edited by Robert de Vaugondy, that the obstacles that surrounded the detailed practice of globe making in

France were removed. By then the map and globe making firm Robert de Vaugondy had been well established.

Didier Robert de Vaugondy (1723 – 86) came from a family with a long tradition in map making. His father, Gilles Robert de Vaugondy (1686 –1763), Géographe Ordinaire du Roi, was the heir of the stock of Nicolas Sanson (1600 – 67) and his sons, during the seventeenth century the foremost map makers in France. Although the Sansons themselves did not make globes, a cousin, Pierre Du Val (1619 – 82), a French engraver from Abbeville, did publish in about 1666 a globe of which nowadays only a set of gores but no mounted copy is known. The Sanson stock will have been outdated around 1700 and can not have been of much help to Didier Robert de Vaugondy, when he started globe making in 1745 [fig 40]. He first produced a small 7-inch globe, dedicated to Louis XV, a mounted copy of which was presented to the king himself on 1 April 1751. This seems to have been followed by the production of the pair of 18-inch globes. At about the same time plans were made to make a terrestrial globe of 6 foot, in order to reproduce exactly the true shape of the Earth, so clearly shown to be flattened at the poles by the results of the expeditions to Peru and Lapland between 1735 and 1738. Lack of financial support obstructed this plan. Much later, towards the end of his life, Didier would obtain another chance to build a large globe, the globe de Bergevin, with a diameter of 2.6 metres. The more regular production of the house of Robert de Vaugondy included terrestrial and celestial globes of various sizes: 3, 6, 9 and 18 inches, the prices of which depended on the type of decoration applied. When mounted in brass meridians on golden feet, with compasses, 9-inch globes cost 240 livres, whereas

fig 38
Celestial globe by Nicolas Bion
(diameter 7in/18 cm, Paris, 1700)

BERN, HISTORISCHES MUSEUM

*The French instrument maker Nicolas Bion (1652 –1733) was
already famous in his own time for the quality of his scientific
instruments. Not for nothing did Louis XV honour him
with the title of 'Ingénieur du Roi pour les Instruments de
Mathématique'. It is known that there are globes by Bion in
existence with diameters of 5, 7, 9½ and 12½in (12, 18, 24
and 32 cm). His production was not particularly large, and so
his globes are now fairly rare.*

'in cardboard meridians and with black feet' the price amounted to 16 livres (Pelletier, 1987, p.133). There was apparently still a luxury market for globes in France. We note here, by the way, that to make brass meridians and stands was the exclusive right of the instrument makers or 'fondeurs'. For instance, the meridians of the globe of 1751, offered to Louis XV and mentioned above, were made by Joseph-Simon Guibot, an apprentice of Delure.

In the last quarter of the eighteenth century the publishing house of Robert de Vaugondy split up and part of it was taken over by Jean Fortin (1750–1831), a publisher and instrument maker who issued two pairs of globes of 8 and 12 inches, as well as a much smaller globe for his armillary spheres. Fortin must also be credited with the publication of a number of celestial atlases through which the new star catalogue of the English astronomer John Flamsteed (1646–1719) became known in France. Flamsteed's catalogue would become the main source for the star positions to be depicted on celestial globes of the second half of the eighteenth century (see chapter 7).

fig 39 ▷

Gores of the terrestrial globe by Jean-Baptiste Delure (Paris, 1707)

ROTTERDAM, MARITIEM MUSEUM 'PRINS HENDRIK';
PHOTO: ERIK DE GOEDEREN

The globe and instrument makers on the Quai de l'Horloge formed an independent group, and many of them were related to each other. The daughter of Jean-Baptiste Delure (d.1736), for example, was married to the son of Nicolas Bion. Of Delure's work, we only know this sheet of gores of a terrestrial globe with a diameter of 8 inches (21 cm). An innovation on the map, which was found with increasing frequency in the eighteenth century, is the addition of the routes of the explorers. Delure only showed these in the Pacific Ocean and the Indian Ocean. The oldest route is Magellan's (1519–22), and the most recent to be drawn in is that followed by William Dampier in 1686.

◁ *fig 40*

Cartouche of the terrestrial globe by Didier Robert de Vaugondy (diameter 19in/40cm, Paris, 1751)

ANTWERP, PLANTIN-MORETUS MUSEUM

The pair of globes that Didier Robert de Vaugondy (1723–86) made at the special request of Louis XV was larger than all globes previously published in France. Globe makers always paid a good deal of attention to the artistic execution of their products. In the eighteenth century, the decorative elements on the sphere were limited solely to the cartouches. Some globe makers employed special designers and engravers to carry out the decoration. The cartography of this terrestrial globe by Didier Robert de Vaugondy was engraved by Guillaume de la Haye; the design and engraving of the title cartouche in particular were the work of the artist Gobin. On either side of the title, he drew allegorical representations of the land and the sea, which flow into each other under the title. In a cloud above sits Fame with the coat of arms of the French king.

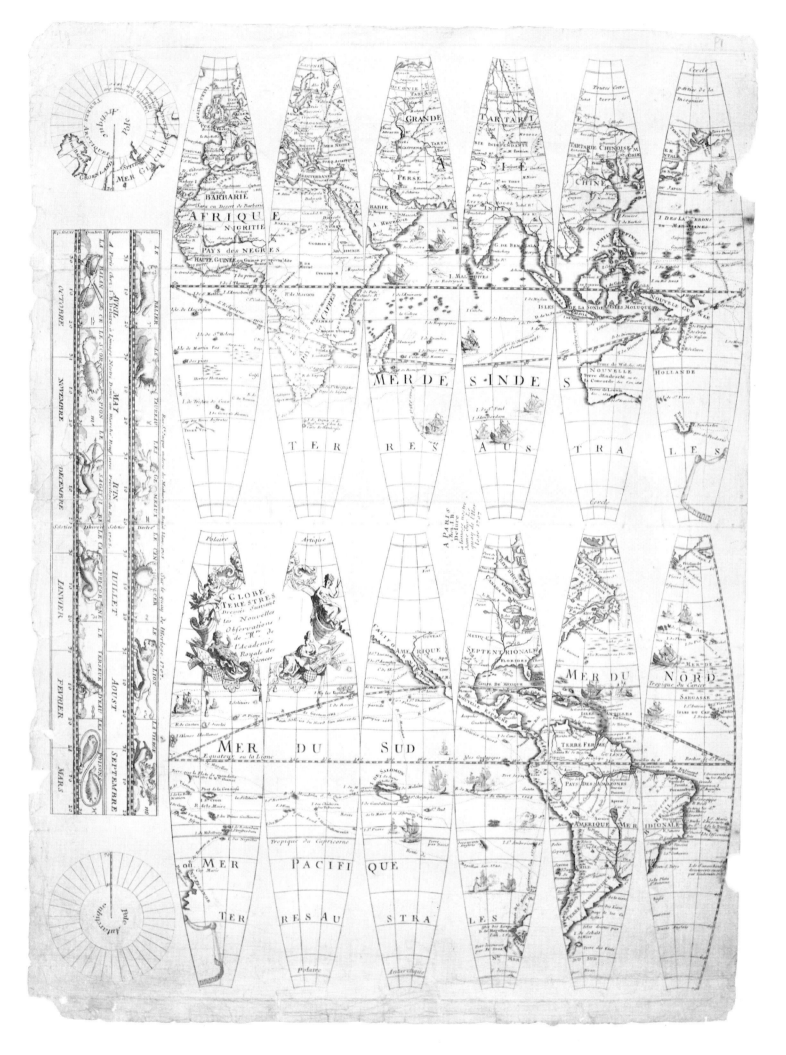

The most successful French entrepreneur in maps and globes was without doubt Charles-François Delamarche (1740–1817). His globes are usually provided with wooden meridians and stands and for that reason could meet the demand for cheap globes [pls 15 and 16]. Delamarche not only took over the shop owned by Jean Fortin but also the remaining part of the workshop of Robert de Vaugondy. He rightly could call himself 'successeur de MM. Sanson et Robert de Vaugondi, Géographes du Roi, et de M. Fortin, Ingénieur-mécanicien du Roi pour les globes et les sphères'. Later he also incorporated the stock of Jean Lattré (*fl. c.*1750–1800), the publisher of a pair of globes designed by the hydrographer Rigobert Bonne (1727–95) and the astronomer Joseph-Jérôme de Lalande (1732–1807) [pl 17 and fig 41]. In 1817 Félix Delamarche succeeded his father and continued the business until the firm went over to Gosselin who had become its manager in 1848. For some time Delamarche junior cooperated with Charles Dien, Sr whose son also produced a number of creditable globes later in the nineteenth century.

plate 16 ▷

Pair of 7in (18 cm) globes by Charles-François Delamarche in a box with parts of a multi-functional planetarium (1808)

GRONINGEN, UNIVERSITEITSMUSEUM; PHOTO: ERIK DE GOEDEREN

The eighteenth century saw a great revival in the public's interest in the natural sciences. Many scientific societies arranged meetings, with readings and demonstrations. The planetarium – a mechanical model of the movements of the heavenly bodies in the solar system – was an aid to understanding astronomy. Special demonstration models included the tellurium and the lunarium, which focused on the movements of the Earth and of the Moon respectively. The Amsterdam instrument maker Hartog van Laun (c.1752/54–1815) and his sons made various complicated devices in parts, out of which a planetarium, a tellurium or a lunarium could easily be put together. These parts are preserved in a wooden box and included a pair of globes. Van Laun first used globes made by Valk, but then later used the newer globes by Delamarche.

◁ *fig 41*

Pair of globes by Bonne and Lalande in a tellurium (globe diameter 6in/15 cm, Paris, 1775 and 1783 respectively)

BRUSSELS, KONINKLIJKE MUSEA VOOR KUNST EN GESCHIEDENIS/MUSÉES ROYAUX D'ART ET D'HISTOIRE: PHOTO: KONINKLIJK INSTITUUT VOOR HET KUNSTPATRIMONIUM/ INSTITUT ROYAL DU PATRIMOINE ARTISTIQUE

These globes made by the Paris engraver and publisher Jean Lattré in 1775 are known as the Bonne and Lalande pair of globes. Rigobert Bonne (1727–95) was the author of the terrestrial globe and Joseph-Jérôme de Lalande (1732–1807) made the celestial globe. The fame of these two academics ensured that this pair is known by their own names and not that of the publisher. This was also encouraged by the appearance at the same time of the brochure Nouveaux globes, célestes et terrestres, d'un pied diamètre, par M. de la Lande et M. Bonne. *Apart from the original edition 1 foot in diameter (31 cm), Lattré engraved smaller pairs of 8- and 6-inch (21 and 15 cm) diameters. The smallest pair was used in this twin globe combination, designed to illustrate the seasons. The instrument was designed by Abbé Grenet and built by Richter, an instrument maker who worked in Paris in the 1790s.*

plate 17
**Celestial globe by Joseph-Jérôme de Lalande,
published by Jean Lattré
(diameter 8in/21cm, Paris, 1775)**

VIENNA, PRIVATE COLLECTION

*The elegant wooden base of this celestial
globe was probably made as a special
commission. Like Delamarche later, Jean
Lattré (fl.c.1750 –1800) normally
supplied his globes on a single leg
[see pl 15]. Joseph-Jérôme de Lalande
(1732 –1807), the Director of the Paris
Observatory, made use of the celestial
globe to pay tribute to a friend, the
astronomer Charles Messier
(1730 –1817), known mainly for his
catalogue of nebulae and star clusters.
The tribute was in the form of the
introduction of a new constellation:
Custos Messium, the guardian of the
harvest, or, in French 'Le Messier'.
On his larger celestial globe of 1779
(diameter 12in/31 cm), Lalande drew
a second new constellation, Taurus
Poniatowski (Bull of Poniatowski),
which was introduced in 1777 by the
Polish astronomer Martin Odlanicky
Poczobut in honour of the Polish King
Stanislas Poniatowsky II. Bode's atlas of
the sky Uranographia, of 1801,
includes another three constellations
introduced by Lalande, and Lalande's cat
is immortalized in the constellation Felis.*

plates 18 and 19

Pair of 2-foot globes by Anders Åkerman (diameter 23 in/59 cm, Uppsala, 1766)

The largest pair of globes by Åkerman appeared in 1766. The publication of this pair also attracted attention outside Sweden. A review appeared in the Neuen critischen Nachrichten *in* Greifswald. *The terrestrial globe is interesting from a cartographical point of view since it is one of the first modern maps to show the Torres Strait (between Australia and New Guinea). After its discovery in 1606, this strait had fallen into complete oblivion. Under the influence of the geographer, Torbern Olaf Bergman, one of the founders of the Cosmographical Society, various thematic elements from physical geography were added to the map, such as the vegetation (woods), the direction of trade winds and monsoons, and the ocean currents.*

plate 20
Pocket globe by Johann Baptist Homann
(diameter 2½in/6.5 cm, Nuremberg, *c.*1715)

LONDON, TREVOR PHILIP & SONS LTD

We only know of one pair of globes produced by Johann Baptist
Homann (1664–1724), the greatest eighteenth-century
cartographical publisher in Nuremberg. In view of his close
collaboration with Doppelmayr, it can be assumed that Homann
also sold his globes [see pl 22 and fig 51]. In addition, he
probably had at his disposal the copper plates of the globes by
Georg Christoph Eimmart [see figs 47 and 48], the gores of
which are found in Homann's atlases. The only pair of globes
with Homann's own name on them is a pocket globe of an
unusual type. The terrestrial globe is, as normal, concealed in a
leather casing, with the gores for the celestial globe on the inside.
The constellations are drawn correctly, as they are seen from the
Earth. The unusual thing is that the terrestrial globe is hollow.
The two halves can be screwed apart; the inside is used to conceal
a small armillary sphere, which is not preserved with all copies.

Although most cartographic achievements
by French geographers found their way readily to
French globes, this can not be said of the most
impressive astronomical expedition carried out by
the French astronomer Abbé Nicolas-Louis de Lacaille
(1713 – 62). In the years 1751– 52 he charted the
southern sky at the Cape of Good Hope and catalogued
9,800 southern stars, most of which were of course
telescopic ones, not visible to the naked eye.
In 1754 Lacaille presented a large map to the French
Academy, on which the 1,930 brightest of these stars
are shown together with fourteen newly invented
constellation figures. Like other non-Ptolemaic
constellation figures introduced by Plancius at the
beginning and by Hevelius by the end of the
seventeenth century, those introduced by Lacaille
represent the cultural image of their time. They are
scientific rather than mythological, showing new tools
of the sciences, such as the microscope and the
telescope and of the arts, such as the architect's square
and rule. These new constellations were readily
accepted by foreign makers. They are also encountered
on the celestial globes by the French cartographer
Desnos and the astronomer Lalande, but strangely
enough they are completely ignored by the main
producer of globes in France at the time, Delamarche
[fig 42]. Furthermore, only a few of them are shown on
the celestial globes produced by Dien junior in the
nineteenth century.

fig42
**Celestial globe of Delamarche
(diameter 7in/18cm, Paris, 1791)**

GRONINGEN, UNIVERSITEITSMUSEUM; PHOTO: ERIK DE GOEDEREN

*The major missing elements on the celestial globe by Delamarche
are the constellations introduced by Abbé de Lacaille in 1754,
along with most of the others that had been introduced since the
seventeenth century. The title of Delamarche's celestial globe
does not name any author, but merely states that the globe has
been drawn on the basis of the most recent observations 'des plus
celebres astronomes de ce temps'. Since the astronomer Charles
Messier is named on Delamarche's larger globes, it is possible
that he is also responsible for this globe. The text near to the pole
states that Cassini had calculated that the geographical pole
describes a circle around the ecliptical pole in 24,800 years.
This circle is drawn on the globe. Every 15°, it states how many
years will have passed since 1770 by the time the celestial pole
has reached this position.*

ADDENDUM: THE WORKSHOP OF THE SWEDISH ACADEMY

The impact of scientific accomplishments of the
members of the French Academy was soon felt in
many countries. The globes produced by Gerard and
Leonard Valk and later by Covens & Mortier in
Amsterdam are examples (see chapter 3). The globes
produced under the protection of the Swedish
Academy by Anders Åkerman (1723 – 78) also show
influences of the French achievements [pls 18 and 19].
Like the French Academy, the Swedish learned society
actively supported the geographic activities of their
members. The most notable of these activities were the
publication of a comprehensive work on cosmography,
published in Uppsala by the astronomer Friedrich
M. Mallet (on astronomy), S. Insulin (on the customs
of the various races of the world) and the geophysicist

and mineralogist Torbern Olaf Bergman (on the physical description of the Earth). These academicians sought to promote map and globe making in Sweden through the Cosmographical Society, 'Kosmografiska Sällskapet' founded in 1758. It so happened that one of the members, Anders Åkerman, was a capable engraver interested in the mathematical sciences [fig 43]. With the financial backing of the society, Åkerman was enabled to set up a workshop for globes. His first globes, a terrestrial and a celestial one, are dated 1759. The scientific input for the terrestrial globe was provided by publications of Academy members and others, whereas the celestial globes incorporated the latest available star catalogues of Flamsteed and Lacaille. This first pair of globes of 1-foot diameter received the approval of the society and was offered for sale for 120 copper thalers, far less than the price of a foreign globe. With further financial support from the society, for two apprentices, Åkerman continued the production of his globes. In 1762 he designed a pair of 11cm in diameter. The celestial globe appeared in two versions, a convex [fig 44] and a concave one. The latter may have been used for making pocket globes. Four years later, in 1766, a pair of 2-foot globes followed [pls 18 and 19]. With the production of these larger sized globes Åkerman's workshop was under financial pressure despite several more subsidies. Commercially he was clearly not doing well, probably because to serve the local Swedish market his globes had to be too inexpensive. The impoverished Åkerman died in 1778.

Åkerman's workshop became the property of the Swedish State and Fredrik Akrel (1748–1804), engraver and for some time the assistant of Åkerman, was made its head. In 1779 he published a new revised edition of the 1-foot pair of globes, incorporating the latest geographical discoveries, among them those of James Cook, and in the ensuing years improved versions of the other pair of 2-foot globes followed. He also received financial backing to sell his globes at low prices, as well as apprenticeship money for Erik Åkerland [fig 45]. Apparently also his son, Carl Fredrik Akrel (1779–1862), assisted his

father for he took over the workshop after Akrel's death in 1804. Thus the production of Swedish globes continued far into the nineteenth century. At present more than 175 globes from this workshop are known. Most of them are found in Swedish collections. Despite financial upheavals the Swedish Cosmographical Society succeeded in making the globe quite commonplace nationally.

fig 43
Portrait of Anders Åkerman (*c.*1723 – 78)

STOCKHOLM, KUNGL. BIBLIOTEKET

The Kosmografiska Sällskapet (Cosmographical Society) founded in 1758 laid the foundations for the start of Swedish globe and map production. One of their members, the engraver Anders Åkerman (1721–78), was responsible for this. Just one year after starting his work, he had finished his first pair of globes, which were of the standard diameter – about a foot. They were not merely copies of existing globes, but were drawn on the basis of new observations.

85

fig44

Set of gores of the convex celestial globe by Anders Åkerman (diameter 4½in/11 cm, Uppsala, 1762)

STOCKHOLM. KUNGL. BIBLIOTEKET

In order to use the expensive copper plate as economically as possible, Åkerman chose a method of placing the gores on his celestial globe whereby the half-gores of the southern (top) and northern (bottom) hemispheres dovetailed into each other. The result is rather confusing, but it must be remembered that it was never intended that these gores would be seen outside the studio. Åkerman's celestial globes are based on the star catalogue Catalogus Britannicus by John Flamsteed (1646 –1719), the first star catalogue to be based on observations using a telescope published posthumously in 1725. For the southern sky, he also used the catalogue by Abbé Nicolas-Louis de Lacaille, published in 1756. The 14 new constellations that Lacaille had placed on the southern hemisphere are all marked.

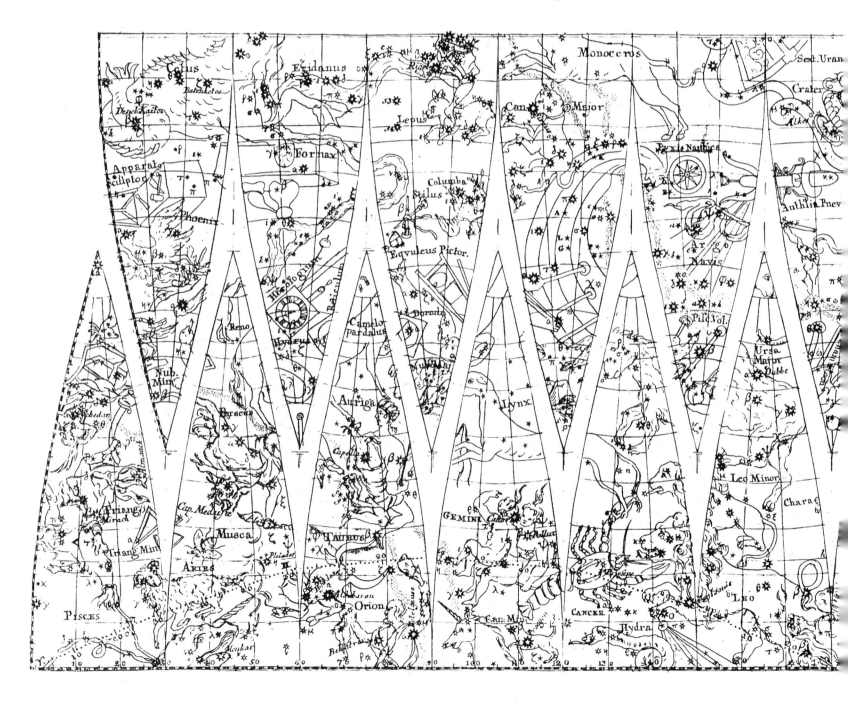

fig 45

Cartouche of the 12-inch terrestrial globe from Åkerman's workshop (Stockholm, 1804)

STOCKHOLM, KUNGL. BIBLIOTEKET

The cartouche of the 1804 edition of the 12-inch (31 cm) terrestrial globe shows the history of this globe workshop. The first edition of the terrestrial globe was published at an unfortunate time, since a few years after publication, the map of the world was greatly expanded by the discoveries of James Cook. Åkerman himself did not publish a revised version. This was done in 1780 by his successor, Frederik Akrel (1748 –1804), who started work in 1779. The last edition, produced by his apprentice, Erik Åkerland, appeared in 1804, the year of Akrel's death. The first edition was produced at the expense of the Cosmographical Society in Uppsala, but after Åkerman's death, production continued under the auspices of the Royal Academy of Sciences in Stockholm.

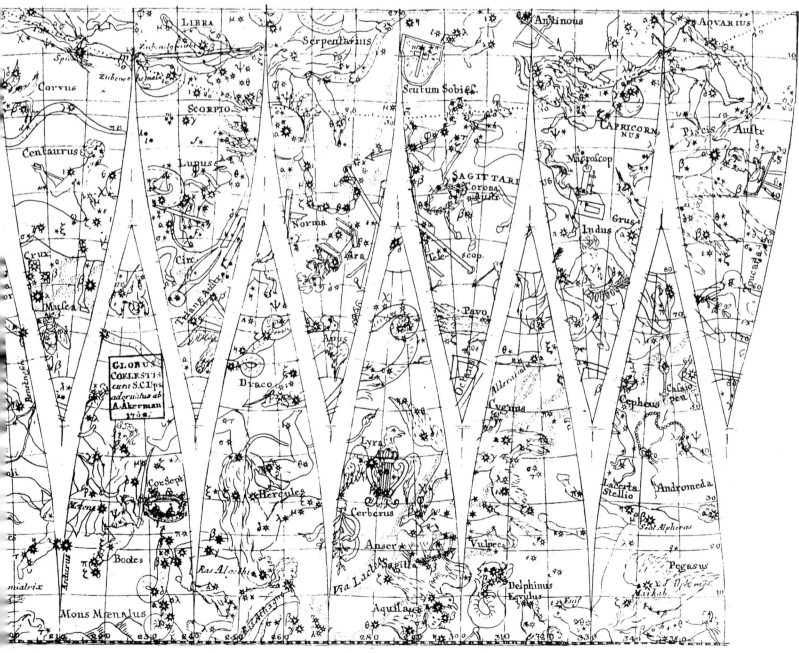

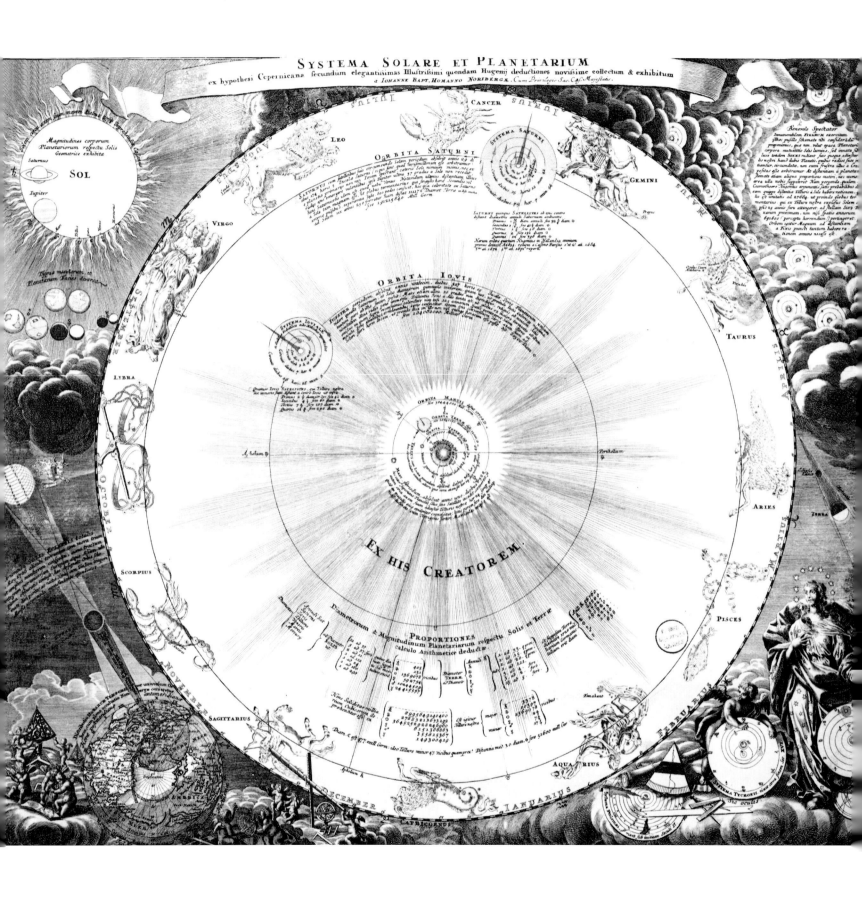

SYSTEMA SOLARE ET PLANETARIUM

ex hypothesi Copernicana secundum elegantissimas Illustrissimi quondam Hugenij deductiones novissime collectum & exhibitum
a IOHANNE BAPT. HOMANNO NORIBERGÆ. Cum Privilegio Sac. Cæs. Majestatis.

EX HIS CREATOREM.

Chapter 6

GERMANY:

Globes and the Enlightenment

fig 46

The Copernican world system according to Christiaan Huygens, published by Johann Baptist Homann (Nuremberg, *c.*1707)

The representation of the solar system according to Copernicus's world view is mainly based on the description of it in the Kosmotheoros of Christiaan Huygens (1629 – 95). It may be that J. G. Doppelmayr (1671?–1750) was also involved, as he wrote explanatory notes for this sheet. The incident that prompted its publication was the solar eclipse of 12 May 1706, which could be seen in many parts of Europe. The bottom left of the page gives an explanation of this solar eclipse. The bottom right shows Urania, the muse of Astronomy with the three representations of the solar system: on the left, the ancient model of Ptolemy, covered by modern instruments, then Tycho Brahe's model of the solar system as seen through observations ('sic oculis') and the new 'sic ratione' (according to reason). With its many illustrations and drawings explaining astronomical phenomena, broken up by allegorical ornamentation, this sheet shows, with beautiful clarity, the state of the science of astronomy at the beginning of the eighteenth century.

Foremost among the German publishers of geographical and astronomical maps and atlases in the eighteenth century is Johann Baptist Homann (1664 –1724). Although originally a monk he left the cloister and settled in 1688 in Nuremberg, where from 1692 he worked as a map maker and from 1702 had his own publishing office. After Homann's death the firm was taken over by his son and later continued to exist as the 'Homannische Erben' until the middle of the nineteenth century. The early activities of the Homann publishing house reflect the revival of interest in cosmography, and in particular in globe making, in Germany, especially in Nuremberg. Many globes published during the eighteenth century are directly or indirectly associated with the Homann firm. The only globe known to be made by Johann Homann himself is a pocket globe published in about 1705 [pl 20].

Of the various globe makers active in Nuremberg during the Enlightenment Johann Gabriel Doppelmayr (1671?–1750) was the most prolific. For him globe making formed only part of his general efforts to foster the scientific interests and the transmission of knowledge from countries like Holland, England and France into Germany. He carried out astronomical and meteorological observations and experimented with electrical phenomena. These activities combined well with his post, occupied since 1704, as professor of mathematics at the Aegidien Gymnasium at Nuremberg. Doppelmayr held this position until his death in 1750 which seemed to have been triggered by an electric shock he received while experimenting with the then newly invented electrical condensors. Among the works he translated into German was Bion's *L'usage des globes célestes et terrestres et des sphères*. Considering that the first booklet devoted to the use of the globe by Johann Schöner was already printed in Nuremberg in 1515, this translation in a way symbolizes the temporary decline of the map and globe making industry in Germany after the sixteenth century.

The revival of globe making in Germany was induced to a large extent by the extensive discussions on the new Copernican, or better Newtonian world system. The advancement of science through the works and ideas of René Descartes and Christiaan Huygens and the increasing significance of scientific instruments like microscopes and telescopes for the exploration of nature, had culminated in the works of Isaac Newton which, 'whether they were correctly understood or not', caused what Isaiah Berlin characterizes as a cultural mutation (Berlin, 1980, p.144). It was the lifelong effort of Doppelmayr to help make the new world system understood, as is best illustrated by his *Ausführlicher Erklärung Uber zwei Homannische Charten, als über das Systeme solare et planetare Copernico-Hugenianum* of 1707 [fig 46]. Doppelmayr's translation of the *Discovery of a new Worlde in the Moone* (1638) by John Wilkins (1619–72), published in 1713 as *Des fürtrefflichen Englishen Bischoffs zu Chester Vertheidigter Copernicus. Oder Curioser und gründlicher Beweiss der Copernicanischen Grundsätze*, is another work that served this purpose. His own major cartographical work, *Atlas novus coelestia* of 1742, is a unique collection of educational maps explaining the basic elements of astronomy and the history of the solar system very much along the lines set earlier in the seventeenth century by Andreas Cellarius in his *Harmonia Macrocosmica*, the first edition of which was published in 1661 in Amsterdam.

Although since 1704 Doppelmayr had been the advocate of the new science par excellence, his first pair of globes appeared only around 1728. Other less successful globe makers had by that time already attempted to provide for the demand for globes in Germany after the decline of the Dutch globe making industry. The first attempts in this direction were undertaken by the publisher Johann Christoph Weigel (1654–1725) who at the end of the seventeenth century published a new edition of the pair of globes produced originally by Isaak II Habrecht (1589–1633) in Strassburg in 1621 [pl 21]. Notwithstanding some small changes introduced on them by Weigel, these globes remained outdated.

This publication therefore was soon followed by a newly designed pair of globes, an initiative of the Nuremberg astronomer Georg Christoph Eimmart (1638–1705). He is especially remembered for the private astronomical observatory he built outside Nuremberg, which he equipped with up-to-date astronomical instruments, many of which he had built himself. The production of his globes was never a success, however, and very few mounted copies are known, presumably because of Eimmart's untimely death in 1705 [figs 47 and 48]. Another globe maker who worked independently of the Homann firm is Johann Ludwig Andreae (1667–1725). Although a priest living outside Nuremberg for most of his life, he published there in 1718 a popular treatise on globes: *Mathemathische und Historische Beschreibung des Welt-Gebäudes Zum nutzlichen Gebrauch Zweyer auf eine neue Art verfertigten Him(m)els- und Erdkugeln*. Copies of such globes had appeared from 1711 on [figs 49 and 50].

One of the more interesting aspects of this treatise on globes is its discussion on the desirability of introducing new constellation figures. Its author preferred to extend existing constellations in order to include new stars over and above the invention of new constellations. For promoting the sale of his globes Andreae included an empty dedication cartouche, to be filled in according to the wishes of his buyers. The

plate 21

Johann Christoph Weigel's edition of the celestial globe by Isaak Habrecht II of 1621 (diameter 8in/20cm, Nuremberg, *c.*1700)

VIENNA, PRIVATE COLLECTION

Isaak Habrecht II (1589 –1633) published his pair of globes, which were closely based on Dutch models, in 1621. The celestial globe is a successor to that produced by Plancius and Van den Keere in about 1612 [see fig 22]. Habrecht added many paths of comets, an innovation that was followed by many Central European globe makers. The terrestrial globe makes use of the maps of Blaeu and Hondius, supplemented by the latest discoveries made by Schouten and Le Maire. The later publisher, Johann Christoph Weigel (1654 –1725), rather carelessly added a few Australian discoveries in about 1700.

plate 22

Pair of globes by Johann Gabriel Doppelmayr and Johann Georg Puschner, re-edited by Wolfgang Paul Jenig (diameter 12½in/32cm, Nuremberg, 1791)

PHOTO: CHRISTIE'S IMAGES

Johann Gabriel Doppelmayr (1671? –1750), working with the engraver and instrument maker Johann Georg Puschner I (1680 –1749), made three pairs of globes: one with a diameter of 12½in (32cm) in 1728, followed two years later by a pair of 8in (20cm) diameter, and finally one of 4in (10cm) diameter in 1736. The fact that his globes were highly prized can be seen

from the long period of time that they were commercially available. A new edition of the largest pair was produced in 1791 by the publisher Wolfgang Paul Jenig (d.1805). The considerable increase in knowledge of the areas around the Pacific Ocean, in particular, meant that Jenig had to bring the maps up to date. He added, among other things, the route of Captain Cook's second journey in search of the antarctic continent, and the portrait of James Cook was also included [see fig 51]. The celestial globe was not altered by him, but he signed the brass meridian ring 'Jenig fecit'.

plate 23

**Pair of globes by Georg Moritz Lowitz
(diameter 5½in/13.5cm, Nuremberg, 1747)**

VIENNA, ÖSTERREICHISCHE NATIONALBIBLIOTHEK

*In 1746, Georg Moritz Lowitz (1722–74) entered the
publishing house of Homann's heirs. He was primarily
responsible for the production of globes, and almost immediately
came up with a plan to make globes with a diameter of
36in (91cm). He did not succeed in this, and the only globes
that he did complete were a terrestrial and celestial globe with
the modest diameter of 5½in (13.5cm). His celestial globe was
based on Flamsteed's star catalogue of 1725, which had not yet
been used by Doppelmayr. Lowitz did not just copy the positions
of the stars from this catalogue, but also the design of the
constellations. The pair of globes was sold until the beginning of
the nineteenth century. The terrestrial globe was then revised by
adding the discoveries of Captain James Cook.*

◁ *plate 24*

**Celestial globe by Johann Elert Bode
(diameter 12in/31cm, Nuremberg, 1790)**

VIENNA, PRIVATE COLLECTION

*The astronomer Johann Elert Bode (1747–1826) was attached
to the Royal Academy of Sciences in Berlin. In 1788, he
announced that he was to produce a pair of globes; he himself
produced the celestial globe (1790) and Daniel Friedrich
Sotzmann designed the terrestrial globe [1792, pl25]. The gores
for both globes were engraved in Berlin, whilst the globes
themselves were manufactured and published by David Beringer
(1756–1821) in Nuremberg, the traditional centre of globe and
instrument production. Bode's globe shows a fundamental
change in cartographical representation. The stars, and not the
constellations, are given most prominence. On older celestial
globes, the figures of the constellations overshadow the stars that
are drawn in. On Bode's globe, however, they are marked with
very subtle thin lines, so that the stars can be seen more easily.*

plate 25 ▷

**Terrestrial globe by Daniel Friedrich Sotzmann
(diameter 12in/31cm, Nuremberg, 1808)**

BERLIN, STAATSBIBLIOTHEK

*Daniel Friedrich Sotzmann (1754–1840) became geographer
of the Royal Academy of Sciences in Berlin in 1786, with the job
of drawing the maps for the Academy. Because of their quality,
his maps were very sought-after and sold well in spite of the high
price in comparison with the normal Nuremberg maps. In 1792,
he designed a terrestrial globe to complement the celestial globe
by Johann Elert Bode of 1790 [pl24]. The gores were engraved
in Berlin by J. W. Schleuen, but production was in the hands of
the Nuremberg publisher, David Beringer. Sotzmann drew in
thirty-six different routes travelled by explorers, and his globe
undoubtedly represents the high point in the illustration of the
history of discoveries. Re-edited versions by Beringer's
successor, Johann Georg Franz (c.1776–1836) appeared in
1804 and 1808. Later, Sotzmann designed globes for the
Geographic Institute in Weimar.*

plates 26 and 27

The first pair of globes by Johann Georg Klinger (diameter 12½in/32 cm, Nuremberg, 1790/92)

The last great globe producer in Nuremberg was the art dealer and engraver Johann Georg Klinger (1764–1806), who published various globes from 1790. His first pair of globes had

a diameter of 12½in (32cm), and these were later followed by smaller globes. The celestial globe of 1790 is based on observations made by the French astronomer Charles Messier (1730–1817). An interesting addition is the note by the constellation Auriga concerning the discovery of the planet Uranus by William Herschel on 13 March 1781. In honour of this discovery, Maximilian Hell placed Herschel's large and small telescopes between the constellations (1789) – and these are also shown on Klinger's celestial globe. The terrestrial globe, dated 1792, was designed by Johann Wolfgang Müller (1765–1828), who used the most modern maps, so that his globes included, among other things, the results of James Cook's three voyages of discovery to the Pacific Ocean (1768 – 80), Samuel Hearne's journey to the north coast of America (1770–72) and Charles Duncan's journey to the Pacific (1788 – 89).

plate 28

Small terrestrial globe with box and prints by Carl Bauer (diameter 2in/4.3cm, Nuremberg, *c.*1825)

UTRECHT, UNIVERSITEITSMUSEUM; PHOTO: ERIK DE GOEDEREN

Various globes from Nuremberg were engraved by members of the Bauer family. The father, Johann Bernard Bauer (1752–1839) worked on, for instance, the large pair of globes produced by J. G. Klinger. His son Carl Johann Sigmund Bauer (1780–1857) made globes for the publication by Friedrich Campe (1825). The younger son, Peter Bauer (1783–1847) worked for Klinger's Kunsthandlung. This tiny terrestrial globe, 2in (4.3cm) diameter, is signed 'C. B' and is almost certainly by Carl Bauer. The globe sits in a small box made of board, containing a great number of coloured engravings of costumes and human races. This type of globe can only be regarded as a child's toy with some educational value.

production of globes by Andreae was later continued by his son, Johann Philipp Andreae (*c.*1700 – after 1757), but it is questionable whether he really was as capable as his father in matters concerning globe making. He could not in any way compete with Doppelmayr. Neither could Georg Matthäus Seutter (1678 – 57), who learned the trade from Homann and in 1707 established himself as a publisher in Augsburg, where he also manufactured his globes.

The gores of the Doppelmayr globes were engraved by Johann Georg Puschner I (1680 –1749), who may also have been the maker of the spheres, the meridians and the stands, etc. of these globes. The three pairs, of diameters of 32, 20 and 10 cm, were produced in 1728, 1730 and 1736, respectively. For a long time the Doppelmayr globes dominated the market for relatively cheap globes in Germany. Several updated editions were published in the 1750s and 1790s [pl 22 and fig 51]. Neither Doppelmayr nor Puschner I had a share in these later globes. Their production was first continued, presumably by the son Johann Georg Puschner II, an engraver and instrument maker who is known to have built a planetary machine in 1751. Later in the century the copper plates came into the hands of the Nuremberg publisher Wolfgang Paul Jenig (*d.*1805), who was responsible for the late eighteenth-century editions.

The cartographical activities of the publishing house of Homann in 1746 were institutionalized through the foundation of the 'Kosmographische Gesellschaft' (Cosmographical Society) by Johann Michael Franz (1700 – 61), then the director of the Homann firm. It seems that before 1748 members were mainly collaborators of the publishing house, but afterwards the membership was more general. Among the more noteworthy members were, of course, Doppelmayr and Franz themselves, Georg Moriz Lowitz (1722 – 74) and Johann Tobias Mayer (1723 – 62), all of whom in one way or another were involved in globe making.

Lowitz, a self-made man, designed a pair of globes

while working for the house of Homann (pl 23). In 1750 he followed Doppelmayr as professor of mathematics at the Aegidien Gymnasium, and he left Nuremberg in 1757 to become professor of practical mathematics in Göttingen. In 1767 he moved to St Petersburg, and was brutally murdered by the Cossacks in 1774.

The most well-known scientist of the Nuremberg cosmographical circle is Mayer, the astronomer who became famous for his work on the Moon. In 1765 his lunar tables won his widow an award offered by the British government 'to any Person or Persons as shall Discover the Longitude at sea'. Like Lowitz, Mayer started his cartographical work as an employee of the publishing house of Homann, but in 1750 he left for Göttingen to teach practical mathematics. Although Mayer was not involved in the production of the more traditional terrestrial and celestial globes, in 1750 he announced a lunar globe, to be made by the Cosmographical Society after his own new observations. Unfortunately this Nuremberg lunar globe has never been published.

The only member of the Society who did not actually design a globe was its founder Franz, but his grandson, Johann Georg Franz, Jr (1776 –1836) moved into globe making towards the end of the eighteenth century when he took over the globe production from David Beringer (1756 –1821). The pair of globes, published first by Beringer and later by Franz belong to the finest ever made in Nuremberg. Not only did they surpass the by then outdated Doppelmayr globes, but the quality and design of the stands is equal to that of luxury globes. These globes must have been expensive, and for that reason they are now rare. Their cartographic designs were made by well-known scientists, members of the Berlin Academy. Responsible for the mapping on the celestial globe [pl 24] was the astronomer Johann Elert Bode (1747–1826), and the geographer, Daniel Friedrich Sotzmann (1754 –1840) drew the map of the terrestrial globe [pl 25]. Both globes are scientifically outstanding for their time.

figs 47 and 48

Gores for the northern hemisphere of the terrestrial and the southern hemisphere of the celestial globes by Georg Christoph Eimmart (diameter 12in/30cm, Nuremberg, 1705)

AMSTERDAM, UNIVERSITEITSBIBLIOTHEEK

We only know one set of globe gores by the astronomer Georg Christoph Eimmart (1638–1705), and these may only have been published after his death. The celestial map is based on Hevelius's Uranographia *and is thus very similar to Valk's celestial globe, which took the same source as its model. The map of the terrestrial globe also shows very marked*

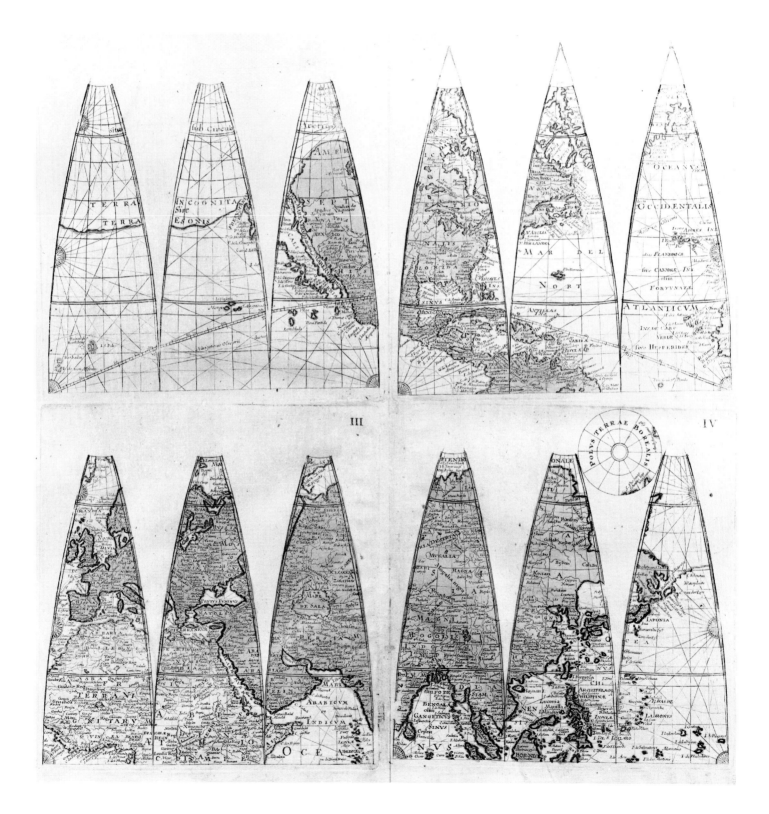

similarities to Valk's globes. The representation of the 'Terra Esonis' between America and Asia and the north-east coast of Siberia is actually identical to the way in which Valk presented these areas; however, the north coast of America is quite different [see fig 25]. It is possible that one of Eimmart's sources was a pair of globes by Valk. The sheets of the gores are mainly to be found in atlases compiled by the great Nuremberg publisher, Johann Baptist Homann. It is notable that the German globe makers of the eighteenth century continued to use Latin for the text. At this time, the French and Italians were using their own languages for their maps and globes.

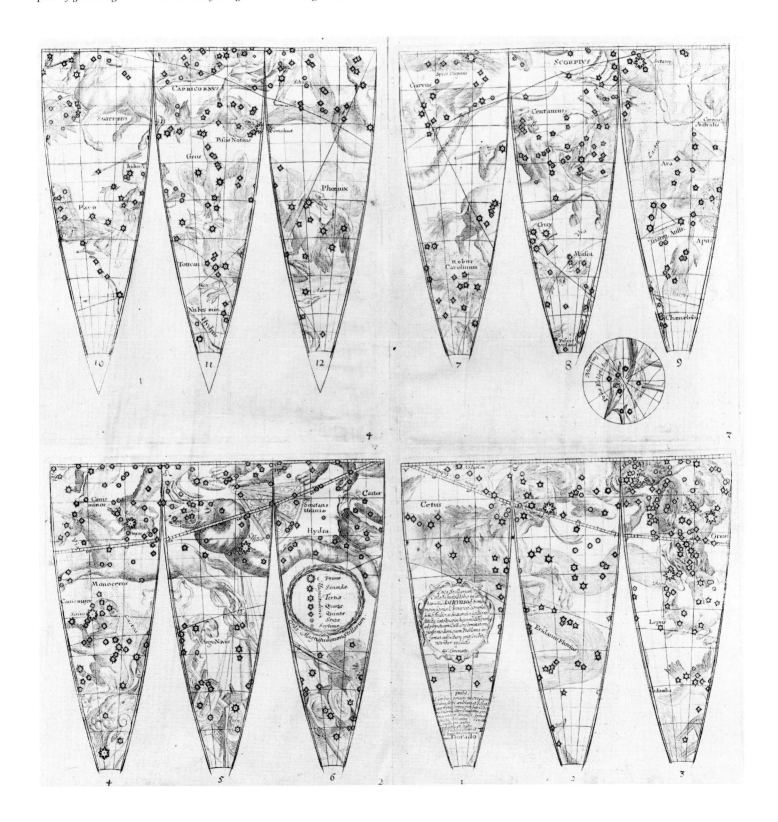

fig49 △

Europe on the 19-inch (48 cm) globe by Johann Ludwig Andreae (Nuremberg, 1715)

MUNICH, DEUTSCHES MUSEUM

In the eighteenth century, the shape of Europe held few secrets, as can clearly be seen on this detail of the terrestrial globe by Johann Ludwig Andreae (1667–1725). Since Ptolemy, the Mediterranean had been drawn too long. From east to west, the sea is about 3,500 kilometres long, or 42° at this latitude. In his Geography, Ptolemy gives a distance of 62° – a third too long. Mercator had already introduced a reduction to 53°; on Andreae's globe, the Mediterranean also stretches over a good 50° instead of 42°. Guillaume Delisle's map of Europe of 1725 finally showed the correct size. In view of the fact that at this time French maps were by far the best, globe makers took the maps of the French cartographer Nicolas de Fer as models.

102

By the end of the eighteenth century the main producer of globes for the domestic market had become the Nuremberg publisher, Johann Georg Klinger (1764–1806). He was the founder of the so-called 'Klinger's Kunsthandlung', a firm that assumed subsequently the names of 'Klinger, Bauer' and 'Klinger and Abel'. Johann Bernard Bauer (1752–1839) was a mechanic and cartographer who started making globes by himself but later produced them in cooperation with the Klinger firm [pl 28]. Others, like Carl Abel [pl 29] and also Johann Adam Bühler (1813–70), an engraver, were involved in the manufacture of globes which continued until far into the nineteenth century. As is clear from the various editions in foreign languages, the later nineteenth-century globes were made to serve an international market. In this the Klinger firm was not alone; other globe factories in Germany and in Central Europe tried similarly to obtain a share of the European market.

fig 50 ▷

Constellations on the 19-inch (48 cm) globe by Johann Ludwig Andreae (Nuremberg, 1715)

MUNICH, DEUTSCHES MUSEUM

Andreae borrowed the cartography for his celestial globes from Coronelli's globes. Johann Ludwig Andreae (1667–1725), who studied theology in Tübingen, lived from 1711 in Esslingen as a mathematician and globe maker. However, he had his globes constructed in the cartographical centre of Nuremberg, where he also lived for a time after 1716. We know of four types of globe from him: they have diameters of 5½, 10, 12 and 19in (14, 25, 30 and 48cm). Some of Andreae's globes also show the name of Samuel Faber (1657–1716), who was the rector of the Aegidien Gymnasium in Nuremberg, although it is not clear what part Faber played in the production of

◁ *fig 51*

Cartouche with portraits of discoverers on the terrestrial globe by Doppelmayr (diameter 12½in/32cm, edition *c.*1790)

MUNICH, DEUTSCHES MUSEUM

The terrestrial globes of Doppelmayr and Puschner pay a good deal of attention to explorers and voyages of discovery. This globe has a large cartouche in the Pacific surrounded by portraits of the explorers. In the most prominent position, at the top centre, stands Martin Behaim, Doppelmayr's fellow townsman and producer of the first terrestrial globe. At his side stand Christopher Columbus and Amerigo Vespucci, followed, in more or less chronological order from top to bottom (on the left and right) by Ferdinand Magellan, Francis Drake, Olivier van Noort, Willem Cornelisz. Schouten, Thomas Cavendish, Joris van Spilbergen, Monsieur de la Salle, William Dampier and R.P. Tachard. Jenig's later re-edited version [pl 22] also included a portrait of Captain James Cook at the very bottom.

103

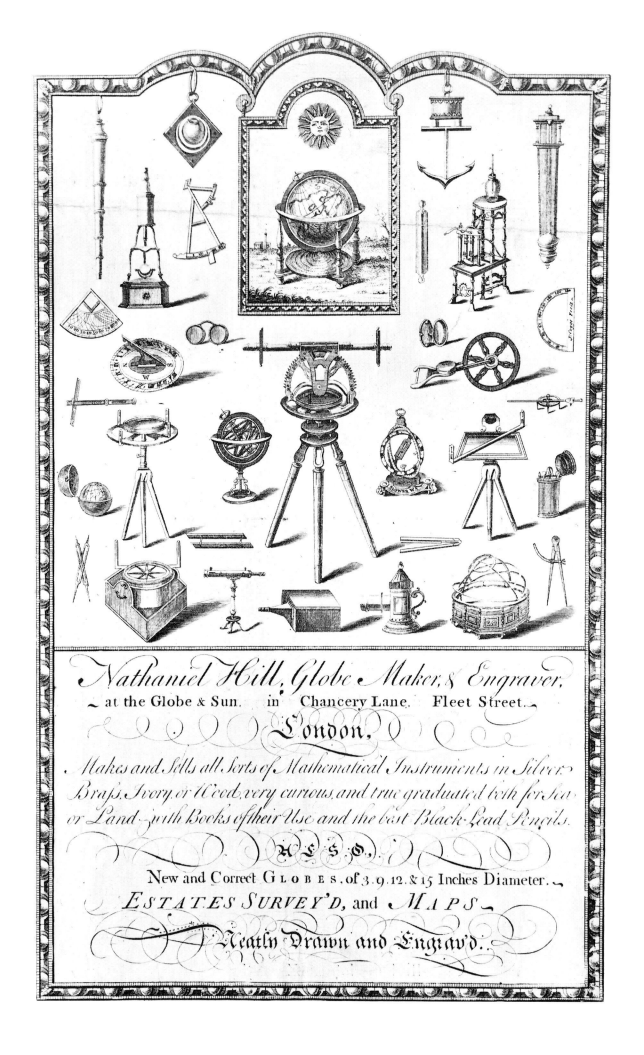

Nathaniel Hill, Globe Maker, & Engraver,

at the Globe & Sun, in Chancery Lane, Fleet Street,

London,

Makes and Sells all Sorts of Mathematical Instruments in Silver, Brass, Ivory, or Wood, very curious, and true graduated both for Sea or Land; with Books of their Use and the best Black-Lead Pencils.

ALSO,

New and Correct GLOBES, of 3.9.12. & 15 Inches Diameter,

ESTATES SURVEY'D, and MAPS

Neatly Drawn and Engrav'd.

Chapter 7

GREAT BRITAIN:

The Orrery and the Globe

fig 52

Trade card of Nathaniel Hill at the sign of the Globe and Sun

LONDON, SCIENCE MUSEUM; PHOTO: COURTESY OF THE TRUSTEES

This magnificent trade card of Nathaniel Hill shows a great variety of mathematical instruments offered for sale. Hill calls himself 'Globe maker & engraver'. In spite of this, his trade card shows that globes only accounted for a small proportion of the range of goods in his shop. Among the large number of instruments, there are two globes: a large globe in the border, top centre, and a pocket globe on the bottom left. The pocket globes, dated 1754, are almost his only remaining globes. According to the trade card, he also made globes of 9, 12 and 15in (23, 31 and 39cm) diameter.

Around 1700 the triumph of Newtonian experimental philosophy led in England to a boom in an entirely new branch of trade: commercial instrument making. On an economic level this development formed part of the so-called 'consumer revolution' in which an increasing demand for high quality goods offered golden opportunities to master craftsmen, who, unlike their fellow instrument makers in France, were not hindered by regulations of guilds or other protectionist organizations. The demonstration of the natural phenomena and the instruction of the wider public were important goals in the process through which the rise of the instrument making trade came about in the first decades of the eighteenth century. The most impressive educational model was the 'orrery', a complicated geared device for the demonstration of the motions of the planets around the Sun, but all kinds of related machines such as the 'lunaesolarium' and the 'cometarium', were invented and designed to teach the new Newtonian world system.

It is against this background that in England at least for some time the globe making industry developed as a part of the instrument making trade, in strong contrast to the situation in continental Europe where the manufacture of globes took place predominantly within the context of purely cartographic enterprises. The globe is a common feature on the trade card of almost every British instrument maker of note; similarly instruments are a regular feature on the cards of the most notable globe makers in Great Britain during the eighteenth century [fig 52].

During the last decades of the seventeenth century, however, globe making in England still belonged to the cartographical tradition outlined by the map making industry. Their makers Joseph Moxon (1627 – 91), William Berry (1639 –1718), Robert Morden (d.1703) and Philip Lea (fl.1683 –1700) came from the existing map trade. Their skills emerged probably all through one master, Joseph Moxon. Berry, and possibly Morden, were apprenticed to him, and Lea was subsequently apprenticed to Morden in 1675. The motives for these makers to undertake the manufacture of globes are well illustrated by an advertisement in 1675 for a treatise on globes, which at the same time announces their manufacturers: 'Whereas the more accurate observations and discoveries of the late years have very much improved Astronomy and Geography, and forasmuch as there have been no Globes made either in England or Holland since these modern Improvements and Alterations; there is therefore lately set forth Proposals for the publishing of a new size of Globes 30 inches diameter by R. Morden, and W. Berry' (Tyacke, 1978, p.13) [pl 30]. Obviously, Dutch globe makers had by their frequent reuse of old plates lost an important market and Morden and Berry tried to take over. Their stands were still after the Dutch style, as were those for the pair of globes made by another early maker, Leonard Cushee. His globes were apparently sold by Benjamin Cole (1695 –1766), a mathematical instrument maker who in 1748 took over the workshop named 'The Orrery & Globe' of Thomas Wright. In 1731 the latter had together with Richard Cushee (fl.1729 – 32) undertaken the publication of Joseph Harris's book *The Description and Use of the Globes, and the Orrery*, a popular text book in the eighteenth century. Obviously, the activities of the Cushees, Wright and Cole were closely connected, but their precise relationships still need to be clarified.

plate 29

Terrestrial globe (Dutch edition) in a box, published by Carl Abel of J.G. Klinger's 'Kunsthandlung'

UTRECHT, UNIVERSITEITSMUSEUM; PHOTO: ERIK DE GOEDEREN

After the death of Johann Georg Klinger, his widow continued to run his firm under the name 'J. G. Klinger's Kunsthandlung'. In 1831, the company was bought by Johann Paul Dreykorn (1805 –75), who continued to run it under the same name. The merchant Carl Abel, who joined the company in 1852, was less modest; from about this time onwards, the publisher's name on the globes was given as 'C. Abel Klinger'. The company was dissolved after the First World War. The firm produced terrestrial and celestial globes in various sizes and in various languages. The smaller terrestrial globes of 3 and 4in (7.5 and 10 cm) were no longer offered in the form of pocket globes, but were placed in wooden boxes. The educative value of these globes now lay in the cartography, with the distribution of the continents, rather than the explanation of astronomical phenomena, for which the use of meridians and horizons were necessary.

plate 30

Part of the terrestrial globe by Morden, Berry and Lea (diameter 14in/36cm, London, 1683)

A collaboration between three London instrument makers and booksellers led to the production of a terrestrial and a celestial globe, marking the beginning of a national tradition of globe production in England. Robert Morden (d.1703), at the sign of *the Atlas in Cornhill, sold a whole range of globes, spheres, maps and mathematical instruments. He worked a good deal with William Berry (fl.1669–1708), scientific bookseller at the Globe in Charing Cross. Finally, Philip Lea (fl.1666–1700) started working with Morden, and then became an independent instrument maker at the Atlas & Hercules in Cheapside. There are globes with all three of these names, or combinations of two – Morden and Berry or Morden and Lea.*

plate 31

Pocket globe by Joseph Moxon
(diameter 3in/7cm, London, *c.*1670)

BERLIN, KUNSTGEWERBEMUSEUM; PHOTO: BILDARCHIV
PREUSSISCHER KULTURBESITZ

The London globe maker Joseph Moxon (1627 – 91) is regarded
as the inventor of the pocket globe, a 'gadget' for amateurs which
was very fashionable, in England in particular, in the second half
of the eighteenth century and the early nineteenth century. The
version of Moxon's pocket globe in the Kunstgewerbemuseum in
Berlin was a present to Friedrich I, Elector of Brandenburg and
King of Prussia, given on the occasion of the visit by Queen
Anne. It is therefore quite unusual – the case is covered with
shagreen leather and decorated with brass ornaments, including
Friedrich's monogram.

Of the early English globe makers, Joseph Moxon is the most important figure in the history of globes, because he was the originator of a new phenomenon in globe making, the pocket globe, although strictly speaking he was not their inventor. Joseph Moxon started making globes in the middle of the seventeenth century, but his first pocket globe dates from around 1680. Although in the eighteenth-century pocket globes were also made by continental makers, it was in England that this type of globe really became popular and was even mass-produced. Originally the attraction of the pocket globe may have been the price, yet the pocket globe is more than a cheap small globe. When its protective case, covered on the inside with gores of the celestial hemispheres, is opened a treasure is revealed, showing the whole world on a very small scale. A miniaturized world as shown by the pocket globe has a symbolic value, which is borne out by the luxury pocket globe Moxon made for Queen Anne, to be offered to the King of Prussia [pl 31]. It is precisely this feature that made the pocket globe such an attractive item then and now. After Moxon, pocket globes were produced by a variety of makers: Charles Price, John Senex, Richard Cushee, Nathaniel Hill, N. Lane, the Adams family, J. & W. Cary, etc.

Before turning to larger sized globes let us mention the one advantage that the pocket globe has over the more traditional pair of globes that were hitherto produced: the concave starry sky. Previously we explained the unnatural feature of the model of the heavenly sky as presented by the traditional celestial globe (see chapter 1): the human constellation figures are not depicted as they are placed or 'seen' in the sky. For that reason celestial globes were unsuitable for the purpose of practical observation, but rather served to teach the various constellation figures and to solve all kinds of astronomical problems like the rising and the setting of the stars. The concave form of the pocket globe on the other hand allows the starry sky to be presented as it is seen above our heads [fig 53]. Yet, so accustomed were makers to the image of the celestial sky as presented on a traditional globe that often pocket globes, including those of Moxon [compare pl 31 and fig 53], still show

plate 32

Pair of 18in (46 cm) globes by George Adams in the second edition by Dudley Adams (diameter 18in/46 cm, London, 1789)

PRIVATE COLLECTION; PHOTO: ERIK DE GOEDEREN

In 1766, George Adams (1709–72) published A Treatise Describing and Explaining the Construction and Use of new Celestial and Terrestrial Globes, *almost at the same time as his pair of 18-inch globes. Adams, one of the most important English instrument makers in the second half of the eighteenth century, had designed a new mounting for globes, whereby the globe could be used more for demonstration purposes. Adams had also paid attention to the cartography, so that the trade winds and monsoons were shown on the terrestrial globe using arrows, following Price and Senex. On the celestial globe, the figures are shown with much less emphasis than on older globes. The stars are indicated by a Greek letter, following the system developed by Johann Bayer in 1603, so that each star was given the name of the constellation and a letter from the Greek alphabet. Adams is one of the first globe makers to use this notation on a celestial globe.*

the celestial sky in globe view, i.e. like a celestial globe turned outside in, and not according to the sky overhead. This phenomenon is not only encountered in pocket globes but also in early presentations of the celestial sky painted on vaults.

fig 53
**Pocket globe by Richard Cushee
(diameter 3 in/7 cm, London, 1731)**

PHOTO: COURTESY OF SOTHEBY'S, LONDON

Richard Cushee (fl. 1729 – 32) worked as a surveyor and globe maker in the Globe and Sun *between St Dunstan's Church and Chancery Lane in London. His pocket globe is dated 1731. The gores for the celestial globe are concave, drawn as seen from the inside. This can be clearly seen from the Great Bear, looking right. In the global view, the head of this constellation points leftwards. It is known that Cushee mirrored his figures: even on his concave celestial globe, the human figures are seen backwards. The constellations also include those introduced by Hevelius; next to the Great Bear, we can see Hevelius's sharp-eyed Lynx [see fig 26].*

The most successful English globe maker after Moxon, who stood at the beginning of a new branch of globe producers in Britain, is John Senex (*d*. 1740). He started as a stationer and from there moved into map making. In 1706 he and Charles Price (active 1697 – *d*. 1733), who had been apprenticed to John Seller (active 1660 – *d*. 1697), advertised their first 'New pair of Globes, Twelve Inches Diameter' (Tyacke, 1978, p.89). Senex and Price also published a pocket globe together. It is not clear how the collaboration between Senex and Price, which lasted from 1706 until 1710, was actually arranged. When it ended they both continued to publish globes, but it seems that Senex was the more successful of the two [fig 54]. Charles Price ended up in 1731 in Fleet Street prison and died in 1733, whereas Senex at his death in 1740 seems to have left his widow reasonably well off. After Senex's demise his wife continued the sale of his globes until 1755 when his copper plates, moulds and tools were bought by James Ferguson (1710 – 76), with the exception of those for Senex's own pocket globe (the unaltered 'celestial' plates of Senex–Price as well as his newly engraved 'terrestrial' plates) which were acquired by George Adams (1704 – 72).

With Ferguson's move into globe making the globe soon became part of the regular stock of scientific instruments offered to the public by London makers.

In the history of scientific instruments James Ferguson is remembered mainly for his popularization of science, in particular the new Newtonian astronomy, by using perspicaciously designed demonstration models. For his lectures upon such matters he expected his readers to possess a common globe. His 'improved celestial globe' is just such a common traditional globe, but some elements have been added to it in order to make it suitable for the demonstration of the Harvest Moon, the apparent delay in the rising time of the Moon in the autumn.

One of the demands of a successful business is the ability to manage but, as John Millburn notes, to do so was a little out of character for Ferguson. In 1757 therefore Ferguson had to give up globe making and his copper plates were transferred to Benjamin Martin (1704 – 82), a travelling lecturer, who moved into instrument making in 1755 – 56. For more than two decades the 'Senex' globes figured prominently in his catalogues and so the globe became well established as a product of the instrument making trade. Other makers, like George Adams, Sr in around 1765, followed suit and designed globes to be included in their stock [pl 32]. Adams's introduction of a new pair of globes of 18-inch diameter increased the antagonism between the two instrument makers. Martin attacked Adams as 'a Person most miserably unskilled in the Art and mystery of Globe Making' (Brown, 1985, p.24). The 'improved' mounting proposed by George Adams for his globes was described by Martin as 'a more deffective construction, more difficult to use . . . than any of the usual construction' (Brown, 1985, p.24). Yet Adams's globes were quite successful, not only in England but also abroad. Adams's celestial globes were based on the recent star catalogue of John Flamsteed (1646 –1719), the Royal astronomer at the Greenwich Observatory, who through his use of instruments with telescopic sights

fig 54

The British Isles as shown on the terrestrial globe by John Senex (diameter 16in/41.5cm, London, *c.*1720)

PARIS, BIBLIOTHÈQUE NATIONALE

The cartographer and engraver John Senex (d.1740) at The Globe *in Fleet Street advertised his first globes in the* London Gazette *in May 1706, where he offered a 12-inch pair of globes. In addition to this pair, he published globes of 3, 9 and 16in (7, 23 and 41.5cm) diameter. In his* Treatise on the description and use of both globes *of 1718, he announced the production of a pair of globes of 26in (68cm) diameter. He used little arrows and wavy lines to indicate the trade winds and monsoons on his terrestrial globes. This method was used before by Senex's partner Charles Price for his map of the world and pocket globes of 1711. In 1728, Senex was made a Fellow of the Royal Society, and after this date added the abbreviation 'F.R.S.' after his name.*

considerably improved the precision of measurement. Adams also employed the most recent star catalogue of the southern stars of Abbé Nicolas-Louis de Lacaille (1756), which had replaced the one compiled by Edmond Halley (1656–1742) in 1678. Later editions of the Adams globes also included the fascinating Australasian discoveries by Captain James Cook (1728–79). With the travels of James Cook, in the years 1768–71, 1772–75 and 1776–80, the era of worldwide maritime exploration of our planet ended. From now on the attention of explorers would be concentrated predominantly on the interior of the still largely unknown land masses that bound the oceans.

The globes published by Martin, using Senex's plates, were outdated. Martin therefore had every reason to be

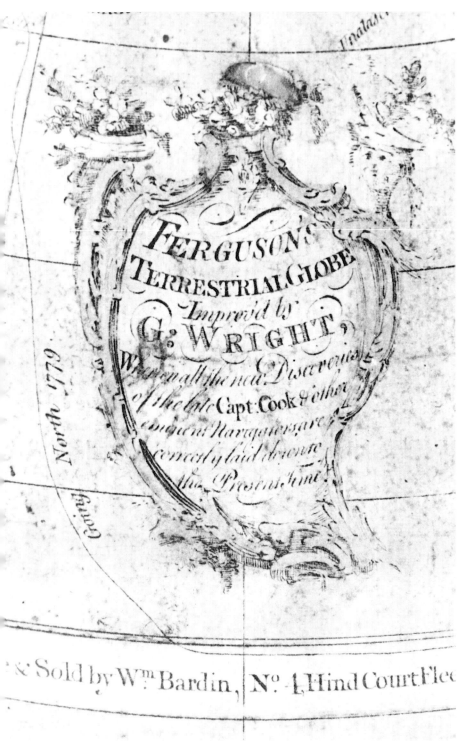

fig 55
Cartouche of Ferguson's terrestrial globe, published by William Bardin (diameter 12in/31cm, London, 1782)

PRIVATE COLLECTION; PHOTO: RENÉ VAN DER KROGT

The text in this decorative rococo cartouche Ferguson's Terrestrial Globe Improv'd by G. Wright *and the text below it* Made & Sold by Wm Bardin *give a neat summary of a piece of London globe history in a nutshell. James Ferguson (1710–76), who bought most of the copper plates of Senex's globes in 1755, also made new globes: 'Mr. Senex's terrestrial globe, new drawn and improved... by James Ferguson'. In 1757, he handed the globe trade over to Benjamin Martin (1704–82), although the names 'Senex' and 'Ferguson' remained linked with the globes for commercial reasons. In 1782, Gabriel Wright (d.1803/4), Martin's assistant, drew some new globes, which he still called 'Ferguson's terrestrial globe'. This globe was published by William Bardin (c.1740–98). On it, Wright drew in the routes of Captain James Cook's three voyages. The left of the cartouche shows part of this: 'Going North 1779' is the route of the* Discovery *and the* Resolution *after Captain James Cook had died on Hawaii.*

worried and of course attacked Adams's globes at their most vulnerable point. Thomas Keith, a teacher in mathematics, wrote in 1812 about the efforts made by instrument makers to improve the globe:

'The addition of a few wires, a semicircle of brass, a particular kind of hour circle, &c. which is of no other use on the globe than to enhance the price thereof, has generally been a sufficient inducement for the instrument maker to publish a treatise explanatory of the use of such addition. The more simply the globes are fitted up, and the less they are encumbered with useless wires, &c., the more easily they will be understood by the generality of learners. The most important part of a globe is its external surface.' (Keith, 1812, p.v)

Obviously, by 1812 the cartographic value of globes had come to the fore again and seen from that perspective Keith judged the 'New British Globes' made by Bardin and those globes made by Cary as the best, the plates of all others being outdated [pl 33]. The globes mentioned here stood at the beginning of a new period in British globe making, of which, with the exception of the Bardin firm, relatively little is known. As recent research by John Millburn has shown, the globes made by them are in a way a continuation of the branch of globe making that began with Senex, and was carried on by Ferguson and Martin. In 1782 the assistant of the latter, Gabriel Wright (d.1803/4), who for eighteen years worked in Martin's shop and presumably made the 'Martin' globes, designed a completely new pair of globes in collaboration with

figs 56 and 57
Title of Hill's pocket globe and of its later edition by John Newton (globe: diameter 3in/7cm, London, 1754 and 1783 respectively)

PRIVATE COLLECTION; PHOTO: RENÉ VAN DER KROGT

It often happens that an apparently new globe is actually a re-issue of an older version. Careful study of the cartography can prove that the same copper plates have been used. The pocket globe published by John Newton in 1783 comes into this category. He used the almost thirty year old plates of the pocket globe made by Nathaniel Hill in 1754. He carefully removed the name and date 'Nath. Hill 1754' and replaced them by his own imprint 'J. Newton 1783'. The remaining text in the cartouche stayed the same. The cartography also underwent a face-lift, in that the recent discoveries of Captain Cook were added (Alaska, on the right above the cartouche).

William Bardin (c.1740–98) [pl 43]. These globes, 'made and sold by W. Bardin', were also sold by other instrument makers. To quote Millburn: 'names such as Adams, Dollond, Hurter, Souter and especially W. & S. Jones, are found on what are basically Bardin globes' (Millburn, 1992, p.24). Of the makers and retailers mentioned the firm of William (1763–1831) and Samuel Jones (active 1810) was instrumental in the publication of a new series of globes by the Bardin firm. These 'New British Globes', with diameters of 12 and 18 inches, appeared from 1798 until far into the nineteenth century, the later editions carrying various names: Bardin & Son, W. and T. M. Bardin, and later still, S. S. Edkins, son-in-law to T. M. Bardin.

The firms of William and Samuel Jones, and of Newton & Son, were among the few in the nineteenth century to combine instruments with globes [pl 34 and figs 56 and 57]. Around 1800 the boom in the instrument making industry was over, trade subsided and globe making followed the more established routes outlined by the developments of the map making industry, which involved makers such as John Cary (c.1754–1835), a foremost map seller who collaborated with his brother William (c.1760–1825), an instrument maker. Other globe making firms of the century are Malby and Son, and Charles Smith and Son. The latter was later taken over by George Philip & Son [figs 58 and 59], but little else is known about their production.

fig 58 ▷

**Terrestrial globe by Malby & Son
(diameter 8½in/22cm, London, 1868)**

LONDON, TREVOR PHILIP & SONS LTD

The table globe of Malby & Son is used here in an astronomical demonstration model, illustrating the movement of the sun in relation to the Earth. There is a sun pointer on the ecliptic that can be used to indicate the spot on the Earth which has the Sun vertically overhead. Malby & Son states on all its globes that they are 'manufactured and published under the superintendence of the Society for the Diffusion of Useful Knowledge', a society that was also concerned with the publication of maps. In 1849, Malby published a reissue of the 'Terraqueous Globe' of John Addison, which, with a diameter of 36in (92cm), is possibly the largest English globe of the nineteenth century.

◁ *fig 59*

**Philip's terrestrial globe
(diameter 18in/46cm, London, mid-nineteenth century)**

PHOTO: COURTESY OF SOTHEBY'S, LONDON

George Philip & Son, founded in 1834 and still a major publisher of maps and atlases, started to publish globes in the middle of the nineteenth century. At that time the firm sold globes by Malby, but at the beginning of this century, the firm started to produce globes completely under their own name. The 1912 prospectus advertises globes of 6, 8, 9 and 12in (15, 20, 23 and 36cm) diameter, and an inflatable globe of 40in (102cm) diameter.

Although initially globe making had been mostly restricted to London, towards the end of the eighteenth century the production of globes started in other parts of the British Isles. In 1776 the Scottish practitioners, John Ainslie (1745–1828) and John Miller (1746–1815), tried in vain to raise money through subscription for their globe making venture. At that time competition from London was still too strong and it was only in 1793 that the first Scottish globe was produced by Miller. His pocket globe, a 'New Year's Gift for the instruction and amusement of Young Ladies and Gentlemen' (Simpson, 1987, p.22) is the only one that has survived. In 1804 the first 12-inch terrestrial globe was engraved and published in Edinburgh by James Kirkwood (active from 1774 to 1824), originally a watchmaker. The map was drawn by the mathematician and geographer Robert Scott (d.1803). Later the firm Kirkwood & Son appears to have collaborated for a while with Alexander Donaldson [fl.1799–1828)], but from 1823 the latter established himself independently as a tool maker and globe maker. At about the same time, in 1824, the workshop of Kirkwood & Son burnt down and a new one was set up by the son, Robert Kirkwood. In 1828 he published a new pair of globes and took the lead in Scottish globe making. Donaldson published a 'New Terrestrial Globe' in 1828, engraved by William and Alexander Keith Johnston, who had been apprenticed to Kirkwood until the fire in 1824 when they set up their own workshop. When in the mid-nineteenth century the Kirkwood firm declined the firm W. & A. K. Johnston became the foremost globe producer in Scotland [pl 35].

plate 33

Pair of table globes by John and William Cary (diameter 12in/31cm, London, 1816/1810)

LONDON, TREVOR PHILIP & SONS LTD

John and William Cary published their first globes in 1791, and, with the firms of Bardin and Newton, were soon in command of the English market. From 1791, Cary's globes were supplied in four sizes: 3½, 9, 12 and 21in (9, 23, 31 and 53.5cm), plus a new pair 18in (46cm) in diameter in 1817. Cary and the other English globe makers produced globes in a variety of designs: library globes are mounted in high mahogany stands with three turned, reeded legs, or with a tripod. Table globes, like these, were mounted in a low stand with four legs.

plate 34

Pair of Newton's globes (diameter 15in/38cm, early nineteenth century)

PHOTO: CHRISTIE'S IMAGES

During the first half of the nineteenth century, the firm of Newton – together with Bardin and Cary – occupied a leading position in the manufacture of globes in London. The founder of the firm was John Newton (1759–1844), who published his first globe in 1783. He was an apprentice of Thomas Bateman, successor of Nathaniel Hill. Newton's first globe was a pocket globe made using Hill's copper plates from 1754 [see fig 56]. An earlier edition of the same globe is signed Palmer & Newton. Larger globes did not appear until the beginning of the nineteenth century (including a 12in/31cm globe in 1801). The firm traded under the names of J.&W. Newton, Newton & Son, and Newton, Son & Berry (c.1830). For a long time, the address of the firm was 66 Chancery Lane, London.

◁ plate 35

Celestial globe by Kirkwood and Donaldson (diameter 12in/31cm, Edinburgh, 1818)

EDINBURGH, ROYAL OBSERVATORY

The company of James Kirkwood & Sons (fl.1774–1824) in Edinburgh published its first pair of globes in 1804 and 1806. The author of the cartography was Robert Scott, a teacher of mathematics and astronomy at Musselburgh, east of Edinburgh. The gores were probably engraved by Robert Kirkwood, one of the sons, who was known as a surveyor, cartographer and engraver. In 1818, a new edition of the celestial globe appeared, which no longer features Scott's name; instead, Alexander Donaldson (fl.1799–1828) is given as being Kirkwood's new partner. The gores for the globes were lost in the High Street fire of November 1824, which started in Kirkwood's workshop.

plate 36 ▷

Large library globe by W. & A.K. Johnston (diameter 30in/76cm, Edinburgh and London, c.1902)

PHOTO: CHRISTIE'S IMAGES

The brothers William and Alexander Keith Johnston worked at Kirkwood & Sons until the great fire of 1824. After this, they started publishing atlases and globes on their own and operated successfully until the end of the nineteenth century. Their largest globe was the 30-inch globe. The physical version of this globe was the first one of its kind made in Great Britain, and it won a number of medals at the Great Exhibition. The later version shown here is a reference globe for the modern businessman who needs information about modern means of transport. The oceans are marked with the principal steamship routes and their distances, numerous submerged telegraph routes are indicated, together with those for the Atlantic crossing date (latest date 1901).

plate 37

**Cary's celestial globe with constellation figures
(diameter 21in/53.5cm, London, 1815)**

plate 38

Cary's celestial globe without constellation figures (diameter 18in/46cm, London, 1817)

AMSTERDAM, PRIVATE COLLECTION; PHOTO: ERIK DE GOEDEREN

From the days of antiquity, the constellations were shown on maps of the sky and celestial globes as people, animals and objects. Their elaborate execution often dominated the cartography. In the eighteenth century, people started to see this type of cartography as unscientific and unhelpful. The figures were drawn more and more schematically and faintly and finally disappeared completely. The boundaries between the areas outlined by the constellations are marked with a line. Because such a scientific cartography looked rather less attractive on a globe, Cary supplied celestial globes in two different designs, i.e. with [see pl 37] and, here, without the figures of the constellations.

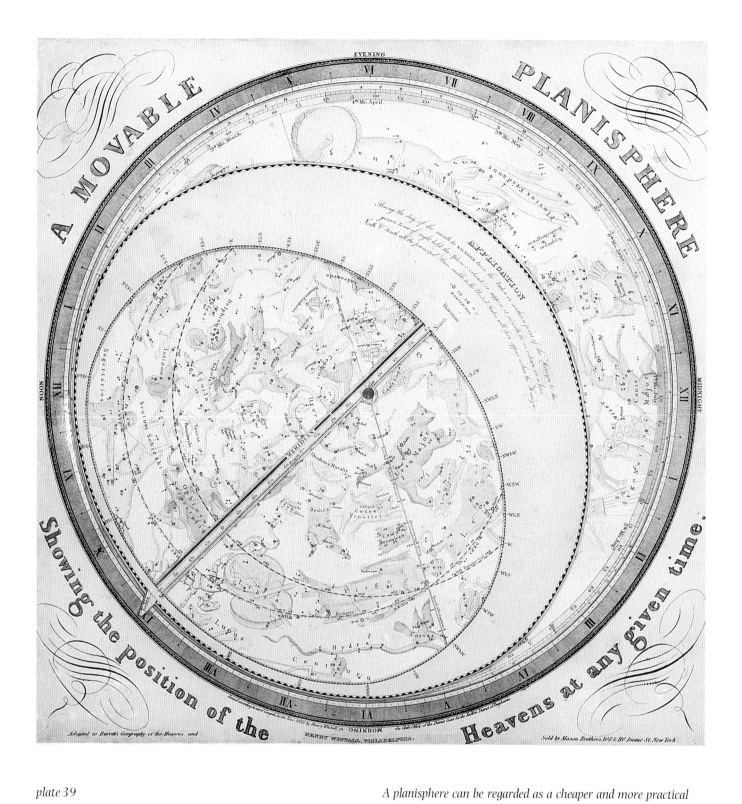

plate 39
Celestial planisphere by Henry Whitall, 1856

LONDON, NATIONAL MARITIME MUSEUM

A planisphere can be regarded as a cheaper and more practical substitute for a celestial globe. Planispheres generally consist of a flat map of the skies, on which a movable disc with a window is fitted. The whole thing is made of board or stiff paper. When the movable disc is set to the desired time, one sees through the window the part of the sky that is visible at the time. Geographical latitude cannot be set, so that a planisphere always has to be used at a particular latitude.

plate 40

**Pair of 3-inch globes by James Wilson and Co.
(Albany, *c.*1820)**

The mounting of this pair of globes on 'bobbin-turned fruitwood table-stands with ebonised bun feet' shows that James Wilson was not influenced by the European tradition of making stands for globes. The globes, although not dated, are signed 'James Wilson and Co'. With this name Wilson traded in Albany, New York, from 1819 to 1822.

plate 41
Pair of 12-inch globes by Josiah Loring and Gilman Joslin (Boston, *c.*1870 and 1833)

LONDON, TREVOR PHILIP & SONS LTD

In 1832, the bookseller and publisher Josiah Loring (1775 – c.1840) started producing globes in Boston. He soon had four sizes available for sale: 4, 10, 12 and 18in (10, 25, 31 and 41 cm), of which the 12-inch globe was the most popular. Both the terrestrial and the celestial globes of this pair were

copied by the engravers William B. Annin and George G. Smith from the globes of the same size produced by C. Smith & Son, London, as stated in the titles. From about 1837, Loring was assisted by Gilman Joslin (1804 – c.1886), who continued to publish Loring's globes under his own name from 1839 onwards. during the 1870s, the engraver George W. Boynton updated the 12-inch terrestrial globe adding, e.g., Dakota Territory (1867) and the united Germany and Italy (1871).

In the nineteenth century the use of the globe in schools led to the introduction of other forms of globes, such as the folding globe by John Betts [fig 60]. This period also saw the decline of the celestial globe, whose practical use was increasingly diminished. The first signs of this are found with the celestial globes by Cary, who provided them with and without the constellation figures drawn in [pls 37 and 38]. This attempt to make the celestial globe more useful could not prevent other, and much more practical instruments, such as movable planispheres being used in practical astronomy [pl 39].

fig 60
Betts's Patent Portable Globe (London, *c.* 1860)

LONDON, BRITISH LIBRARY

The nineteenth century saw the appearance in various places of folding or collapsible globes that were cheaper and easier to store away. One of these globes was Betts's Patent Portable Globe from around 1860. It operates in the same manner as an umbrella. A cloth sphere is mounted on flexible metal struts set around a central metal spindle. When expanded, the globe is 40 centimetres in diameter. The globe was designed by John Betts (fl. 1844 – 63) in the Strand, London, of whom little is known except the fact that he produced educational material for children.

Chapter 8

UNITED STATES:

Globes from the New World

In 1875 Ellen Eliza Fitz (*b.*1836), an American governess working in St John Country, New Brunswick, obtained a patent for a new method of mounting and operating globes [fig 61]. This first design by a woman was published in the subsequent year as: *Handbook of the Terrestrial Globe; or, Guide to Fitz's New Method of Mounting and Operating Globes* (1876). The book was reprinted several times, and in an appendix the technique of making a sphere for a globe was described for the sake of completeness:

'A globe is made of pasted paper, eight or ten layers of this being applied successively to a mould prepared for the purpose. As this coating becomes dry, it shrinks and fits tightly over the mould; from which it is then removed, first being divided into two hemispheres. A turned stick of right length, with a short wire in each end for poles, is now introduced, one end in each hemisphere; and the two shells, being brought together, are secured by gluing their edges. The ball is now hung within a steel semicircle just fitting its exterior, and coated with a composition of glue and whiting. Being made to revolve, the excess of the composition is removed by the circle; and the ball is thus turned smooth and true, after which it is carefully dried.'

As Millburn has pointed out, the source of this description may well have been a publication in 1850

fig 61
'Fitz Globe', published by Ginn & Heath (diameter 12in/31cm, Boston, 1879)

WASHINGTON, D.C., NATIONAL MUSEUM OF AMERICAN HISTORY;
PHOTO: SMITHSONIAN INSTITUTION

The special feature of Fitz's globe is the mounting. This globe can be used to illustrate the course of the sun, the length of day and night and the length of twilight over the whole year. The globe is mounted at an angle of 66.5° on a rotatable disc, with a calendar. The sphere with the indicator shows the position of the sun, whilst the two meridians indicate the twilight zone. This mounting was designed by Ellen Eliza Fitz (b.1836), an American governess from New Brunswick, who obtained a patent for it in 1875. The following year, she published a Handbook of the Terrestrial Globe; or, Guide to Fitz's New Method of Mounting and Operating Globes.

in *Household Words*, edited by Charles Dickens, under the heading 'Illustrations of Cheapness: A Globe' in which the production methods of globes by Messrs Malby and Son were discussed. The method of making a sphere in this way had been published more than once in Europe in the eighteenth century, when the United States of America were still in the process of becoming a nation. By 1867 it was well known among American globe makers. It is nevertheless interesting to note that the method had in fact been worked out independently by the first commercial globe producer in America, James Wilson (1763–1855).

In 1796, the year in which Wilson established himself as a farmer in Bradford, Vermont, he paid a visit to

Dartmouth College, Hanover, N.H. where his attention was drawn to a pair of globes. During the eighteenth century most globes in America were imported from England. The one globe of that period by the surveyor Samuel Lane, demonstrates that globes were occasionally made for specific purposes, but there was no actual globe industry [fig 62]. In his *Thinkers and Tinkers* Silvio A. Bedini reports that at the time Wilson visited Dartmouth College it owned three pairs of globes: a 16-inch pair made by Senex, another pair of 18 inches bought in 1774 (perhaps by George Adams), and a third pair of unknown size and maker. It is not known which of these pairs impressed Wilson most, but the fact is that he returned home with the determination to copy one of them. Bedini relates how

fig 62

The oldest American globe, the 7-inch terrestrial globe by Samuel Lane (diameter 7in/18 cm, *c.*1760)

CONCORD, N.H., NEW HAMPSHIRE HISTORICAL SOCIETY

The oldest known globe made on the American continent is this terrestrial globe from about 1760. The cartography is painted on a solid wooden ball. The mounting of the globe shows clearly that the maker did not have any European models. It was produced by Samuel Lane, a surveyor and shoe maker from Stratham, Massachusetts.

he first made the spheres of the globes out of solid wood, but very quickly introduced a refinement by coating the wooden balls with several layers of paper and cutting the sphere into two hemispheres, the coverings of which were pasted together after removing the wooden ball. The next step in Wilson's increasing expertise was his acquisition of the *Encyclopaedia Britannica* from which he gleaned the necessary geographical and astronomical knowledge. Then, he came to realize that he had to learn how to make gores, i.e. the technique of copper plate engraving. The story Bedini relates illustrates Wilson's determined perseverance: because of lack of money he travelled in vain on foot to Boston, then in vain again to Newburyport, and eventually reached New Haven.

There he met the map engraver Amos Doolittle who was kind enough to help him to master the art of engraving. On the mathematics of gore construction he received, again after a walk, now to Charlestown, Massachusetts, assistance from Jedediah Morse (1761–1826), the author of *Geography Made Easy* (1784), the first American work on this topic.

In making his globes Wilson covered the whole range of arts needed to produce them: he made his own auxiliary instruments ranging from lathes and presses to inks and glues, etc., he made his own spheres, engraved and designed his own gores, he turned his own wooden supports, made the brass quadrants, and even the boxes in which to pack his globes. The earliest

fig 63
Title of the 'New American Terrestrial Globe' by James Wilson (diameter 13in/33cm, Bradford, Vermont, 1811)

WASHINGTON, D.C., NATIONAL MUSEUM OF AMERICAN HISTORY;
PHOTO: SMITHSONIAN INSTITUTION

James Wilson (1763–1855), the first commercial globe maker in America, advertised his globes as being more accurate, particularly as regards the map of America, than the globes that were imported from England. They were also cheaper. The globes made by Wilson, who had taught himself geography and the technique of engraving, are in fact precise and attractive. His first terrestrial globe had a diameter of 13in (33cm) and dates from 1810; a new edition appeared in 1811, followed by the matching celestial globe a year later.

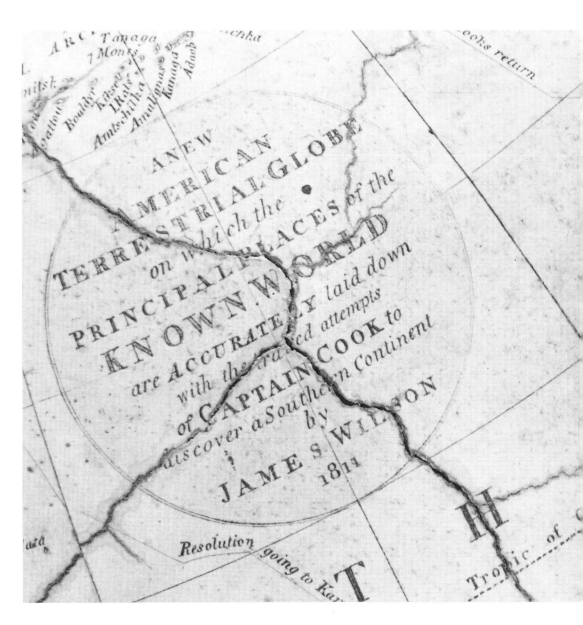

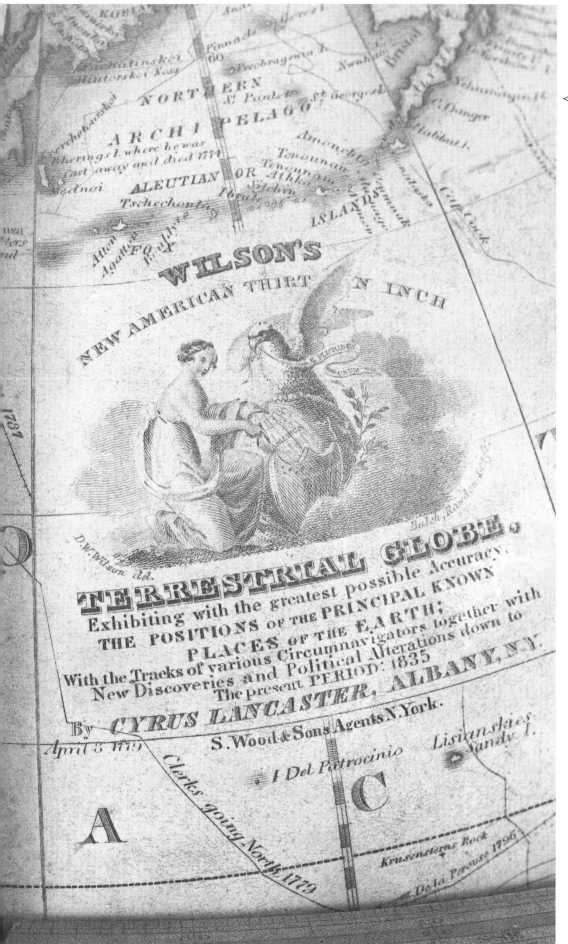

Title of Wilson's 'New American Thirteen-Inch Terrestrial Globe' by Cyrus Lancaster (Albany, 1835)

WASHINGTON, D.C., NATIONAL MUSEUM OF AMERICAN HISTORY; PHOTO: SMITHSONIAN INSTITUTION

From 1826, Cyrus Lancaster (c.1802 – 62) worked for James Wilson & Sons in Albany. After Wilson's two sons John and Samuel died in 1833, Lancaster married Samuel's widow and continued to produce globes under his own name. In 1835, a new edition of the 13-inch globe appeared. The decorative illustration accompanying the title emphasises the American aspects of the globe. The American eagle, holding a tape in its beak with the motto E pluribus unum, sits on a terrestrial globe showing America. In front of the globe stands the American coat of arms, and a female figure holds a pair of compasses to America.

fig 65 ▷

Title of Wilson's 'New Thirteen-Inch Celestial Globe' by Cyrus Lancaster (Albany, 1835)

WASHINGTON, D.C., NATIONAL MUSEUM OF AMERICAN HISTORY; PHOTO: SMITHSONIAN INSTITUTION

With the terrestrial globe, Cyrus Lancaster also published, in 1835, a new edition of Wilson's celestial globe. The original globe by Wilson, from 1812, showed, according to the title, the position of 'nearly 5,000' stars based on the calculations of Maskelyne, Herschel and Wollaston. Lancaster claimed to have drawn in 7,000 stars, although he does not say which source he used for these extra 2,000 stars.

record of globes sold by Wilson is dated 1810 and he must have had some success for in about 1815 he moved to Albany, New York to set up a globe factory [pl 40 and fig 63]. There his sons Samuel and John, and later David, participated in his globe making business which from 1826 on was managed by his future son in law Cyrus Lancaster (c. 1802 – 62) [figs 64 and 65].

The globes made by Wilson certainly appealed to the local market, not only because they were cheaper than the ones imported from England, but also because the delineation on Wilson's terrestrial globes included more accurately the various American territories. As Deborah Warner notices: 'Americans always have been more interested in American geography than in the geography of the rest of the world' (Warner, 1987, p.18). This chauvinistic attitude is certainly true for the first half of the nineteenth century, and quite understandable for people living in a nation in the making. In the course of the nineteenth century the number of States that were united increased steadily. The vivid interest with which American citizens followed this development is well illustrated by the girls of a Quaker school at Westtown, close to Philadelphia, who occupied themselves in drawing and embroidering geographical and astronomical data on silk covered globes, and by the globe made by Elizabeth Mount in 1820 [fig 66].

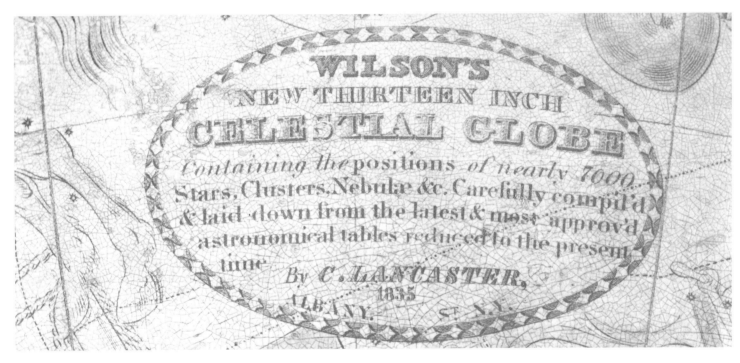

fig 66 ▷
'All states in the union'; the terrestrial globe by Elizabeth Mount
(diameter 20 in/51 cm, c. 1820)

NEW HAVEN, YALE UNIVERSITY ART GALLERY,
MABEL BRADY GARVAN COLLECTION

This is a very detailed terrestrial globe drawn by Elizabeth Mount from Setauket on Long Island in the state of New York. She drew the cartography on paper gores that are stuck onto a papier maché sphere. All the states that made up the United States at that time are shown on the globe.

At the beginning of the nineteenth century, the United States was relatively unexplored, cartographically. When the president of the United States, Thomas Jefferson, negotiated the acquisition of Louisiana in 1803, the greatest land purchase in history, he hardly knew what he was buying [fig 67]. In order to find out, the first American scientific expedition was undertaken by Captain Meriwether Lewis (1774 – 1809) and Captain William Clark (1770 –1838). Jefferson personally provided instructions to search for the source of the Missouri River, to cross the highlands, and to investigate possible communications by water to the Pacific Ocean. Lewis and Clark reached the west coast on 7 November 1805. Later in the nineteenth century other expeditions were undertaken, such as the 'Exploring Expedition under the command of Lieutenant Wilkes of the United States Navy' in 1838 which signifies the growing interest in America for maritime power.

fig 67

Portrait of Thomas Jefferson with a globe after a painting by Rembrandt Peale (1801)

WASHINGTON, D.C., NATIONAL MUSEUM OF AMERICAN HISTORY;
PHOTO: SMITHSONIAN INSTITUTION

The globe with which Thomas Jefferson (1743 –1826) is depicted at the start of his official term as third president of the United States (1801) is not an American product. The first American globe did not appear until 1810, one year after Jefferson was succeeded as president by James Madison.

An early 'Franklin' terrestrial globe by Merriam Moore & Co. (diameter 6in/15cm, Troy, N.Y., *c.*1852)

VIENNA, PRIVATE COLLECTION

'A Six-Inch American Terrestrial Globe comprising the Latest Political Divisions, Discoveries &c.' is the title of this globe, published by Merriam Moore & Co. in Troy, N.Y. On the basis of the political information it gives, the globe can be dated to between 1848 and 1853 (after the Treaty of Guadelupe Hidalgo and the establishment of the Oregon Territory, but before the Gadsden Purchase and the establishment of Washington Territory). The booksellers Merriam & Moore (after 1869, H. B. Nims & Co.) sold globes in five different sizes: 6, 10, 12, 16 and 30in (15, 25, 31, 41 and 76cm). From the end of the 1850s, they are known as Franklin globes, a name possibly derived from Franklin Field (c.1824–1904) who was registered as a globe manufacturer in Troy between 1853 and 1860.

plates 43 and 44
**Globes from a collection in
New England:
Bardin's New British Globes
(18in/46 cm) and
American Franklin globes**

SALEM, MASS., PEABODY & ESSEX MUSEUM

*Nathaniel Bowditch (1773–1838)
from Salem, Massachusetts, made a
number of sea voyages between 1795
and 1803, the last of which was as a
supercargo. He had little interest in the
practical aspects of navigation and
devoted all his free time on board to the
study of the theoretical principles of
navigation. He found an enormous
number of mistakes in the navigational
books used. He put these right in his
New American Practical Navigator,
published in 1802. For this work he was
awarded a Master of Arts degree by
Harvard College in the same year.
Bowditch's library naturally contained a
pair of globes. There were no American
globes at this time, and so he had bought
a pair of the largest New British Globes
by W. & T. M. Bardin (left), via the
London instrument maker W. S. Jones.
The globes are currently owned by the
Peabody & Essex Museum in Salem,
where a pair of 12-inch Franklin globes
and a 6-inch Franklin instructional
globe are also to be found (opposite).
These Franklin globes were published
by Merriam & Moore in Troy, N.Y.,
in the 1850s.*

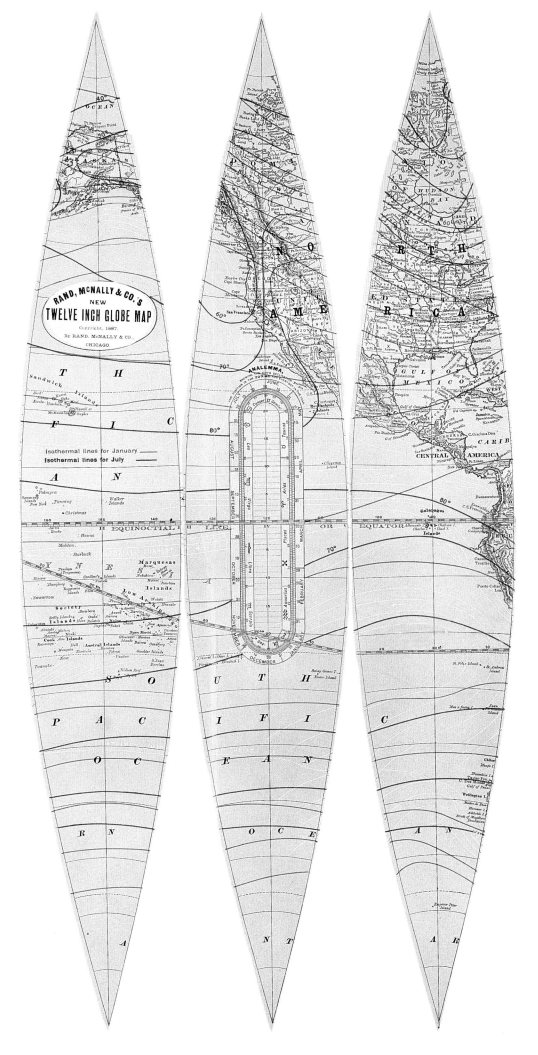

plate 45

The gores of the first known terrestrial globe by Rand McNally (diameter 12in/31cm, Chicago, 1887)

Rand McNally & Co., founded in 1856, is now one of the most well-known cartographical publishers in the United States. The technique of wax engraving, introduced by this firm in 1872, marked a revolution in American map production; the relatively cheap and easy method meant that corrections could be made at any time. However, the first globe by this company did not appear until 1887. An interesting feature is the addition of isothermal lines for January and July.

Some of Wilson's globes have their prime meridian through Washington. In this regard American globe makers were not more chauvinistic than French makers who from Cassini's time onwards drew the prime meridian through Paris, or British makers who drew it initially through London and later through Greenwich. This practice was the result of the fact that the main function of the prime meridian was navigational, not cartographic. In order to determine the longitude at sea, navigators compared the local time on board with that of their own home port. The difference between the two times indicates the difference in longitude with respect to that of the home port. The use of distinct prime meridians for naval purposes by various countries resulted later in the century in a lively debate, in which the possibility of one universal prime meridian was discussed. The battle was won by the British, and since then the majority of makers of terrestrial globes have employed as the prime meridian that of Greenwich.

The demand for American globes was to a large extent stimulated by the teaching of geography, which in the nineteenth century extended to wider groups than in the previous century. Teachers like Jeremiah Moriarty travelled westwards too. In 1789 he advertised in the Kentucky Gazette that in addition to dancing he 'Teaches geography and the use of the globes, having a pair on a new construction with Captain Cooks discoveries' (Bedini, 1975, p.378). In 1815 Harvard College made knowledge of geography an entrance requirement, and some years later it formed part of the public school curriculum. It is therefore not surprising that after Wilson's first successful attempts others started with commercial globe making.

Among the globe makers working in the first half of the nineteenth century the engravers William B. Annin (d.c.1839) and George C. Smith of Boston should be mentioned. Their globes were sold by the bookseller Joseph Loring (1775 – c.1840) under his own name [pl 41]. It was Loring therefore and not

Annin, who in 1838 received a silver medal for these globes. Their sale was later also taken up by another Bostonian bookseller, Gilman Joslin (1804 – c.1886). Another capable engraver was Charles Copley (active 1843 – 69) who in 1852 received a gold medal for his globes at the fair of the American Institute in New York [figs 68 and 69]. Later editions of his globes were traded by the same firm(s) that published the so-called Franklin globes [pls 42, 43 and 44]. These globes were issued by the publishers Merriam & Moore, a firm which in the course of the nineteenth century changed its name frequently. It is still unclear why these globes are called Franklin globes. According to Deborah Warner 'the name may derive from Franklin Field (c.1824 –1904), who is listed as a 'globe manufacturer' in Troy city directories during the period 1853 – 1860' (Warner, 1987, p.63).

figs 68 and 69

A terrestrial and celestial globe gore by Charles Copley (diameter 16 in/41 cm, New York, 1852)

WASHINGTON, D.C., LIBRARY OF CONGRESS, GEOGRAPHY AND MAP DIVISION

An enormous wealth of toponymical detail on the continents is a marked contrast with the relative emptiness of the oceans on the gores for the terrestrial globe produced by Charles Copley (active 1843 – 69). The information on his celestial globe is somewhat more evenly spread. Copley, a cartographer and engraver from Brooklyn, made these globe gores in 1852. His pair of globes was not a great commercial success, although revised versions were published by Moore & Nims and Gilman Joslin until the 1890s.

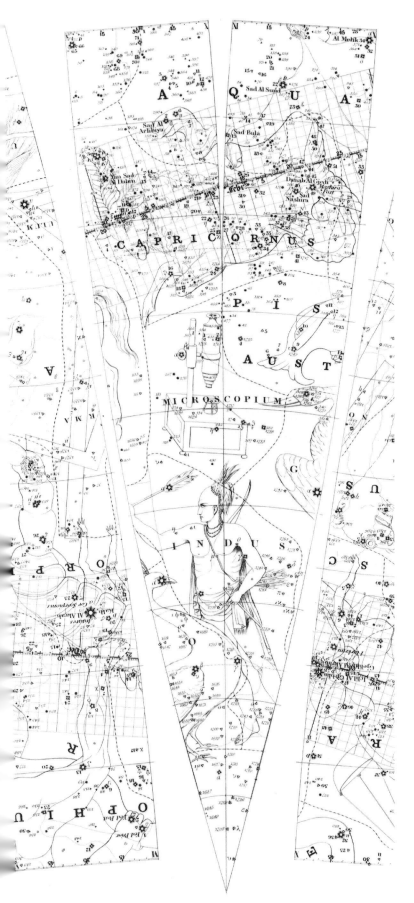

In the second half of the nineteenth century the globe making industry in America developed along the same lines as that of Europe. One of the most influential changes was the use of new printing techniques such as lithography and wax engraving. The German immigrant Joseph Schedler (*fl.* 1850 – 80) started globe making in the fifties, as an activity of the New York lithography firm Schedler & Liebler. Schedler's globes were printed in colour, one of the foremost advantages of the new printing techniques [figs 70 and 71]. The use of wax printing was introduced in America in 1872 by the firm Rand McNally & Co. in Chicago [pl 45]. Their new method was so successful that by the end of the century this firm dominated the American market. In addition to the traditional globes Rand McNally produced several thematic globes, to be discussed in the next chapter.

We conclude this chapter with a few notes on globes that show the trace of an important technological expansion of the nineteenth century, telegraphy. Although telegraphy was not an American invention, it was rapidly taken up in American life, because it allowed messages of all sorts to be communicated very quickly over large distances. The attempts undertaken from 1857 until 1866 to establish a telegraphic link across the Atlantic Ocean fascinated the people in Europe and America, and globes were used for promoting a similar connection across the Pacific [fig 72].

The usefulness of telegraphy for communication purposes was not limited to trade or political business alone. One of its important geodetical applications has been to provide a better way to determine longitude. With the help of telegraphically transmitted time signals observations made in places far apart can be communicated simultaneously, thus improving the methods established by the French astronomer Cassini at the end of the seventeenth century. This improvement, first applied by the US coast survey, soon found its way to Europe. Through the longitude problem the geographical element of time once again became an issue. The discussions which in 1884 led to

141

the adoption of a universal prime meridian, at the same time triggered the introduction of a universal time and in its wake, a world system of time zones and the international date line. Time was still regulated by the daily rotation of the Earth as measured against the stars, very much like it was understood in the sixteenth century when a number of clockwork driven celestial globes was built. The terrestrial and celestial time globes made in the 1870s by Louis-Paul Juvet (1830–1930), originally a jeweller from Switzerland, are in a way late specimens of this tradition of demonstrating the relation between time and the Earth's daily motion.

◁ *fig 70*

Joseph Schedler's terrestrial globe (diameter 6in/15cm, Jersey City 1869)

WASHINGTON, D.C., NATIONAL MUSEUM OF AMERICAN HISTORY: PHOTO: SMITHSONIAN INSTITUTION

The German immigrant Joseph Schedler (fl. 1850 – 80) started producing maps and globes in the 1850s. He carried off three medals with his globes: at the Paris International Exhibition of 1867, the American Institute fair of 1869 and the Vienna International Exhibition of 1873. His globes were sold by the bookseller E. Steiger in New York, whose name is to be found on some editions of the globes. In 1875, he published An Illustrated Manual for the Use of the Terrestrial and Celestial Globes. *At that time, he produced globes in six sizes.*

fig 72 ▷

The Telegraphic Globe by the New York Silicate Book Slate Co. (diameter 12in/31cm, New York, 1872)

WASHINGTON, D.C., LIBRARY OF CONGRESS, GEOGRAPHY AND MAP DIVISION

The first undersea telegraph cable was laid in 1850, providing a connection between England and France. This was followed in 1866 by a telegraph cable under the Atlantic. Almost immediately, plans were made to lay a cable under the Pacific too, so that the network of telegraph cables would encircle the world. In 1872, the New York Silicate Book Slate Co., which actually dealt in slates and blackboards, made a terrestrial globe intended to arouse interest in this telegraph connection across the Pacific. Two possible routes across the Pacific, proposed by Cyrus W. Field, are drawn in on this Telegraphic Globe. These and the existing telegraph lines were specially drawn for the globe by no less a person than Samuel Morse, the inventor of the electromagnetic telegraph (1835).

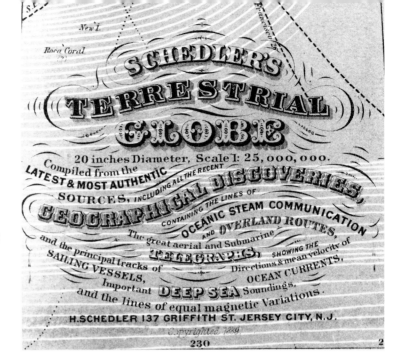

fig 71 ▷

Title of the 20-inch terrestrial globe by Schedler (diameter 20in/51cm, Jersey City, 1889)

WASHINGTON, D.C., LIBRARY OF CONGRESS, GEOGRAPHY AND MAP DIVISION

The largest pair of globes produced by Joseph Schedler in Jersey City had a diameter of 20in (51cm). By making use of a variety of letter types and wavy lines, he was able to make the very long title of this globe into a decorative whole – without making decorative additions! Schedler was one of the first to draw in shipping lines, telegraph lines, ocean currents, depth figures and lines of the same magnetic variation.

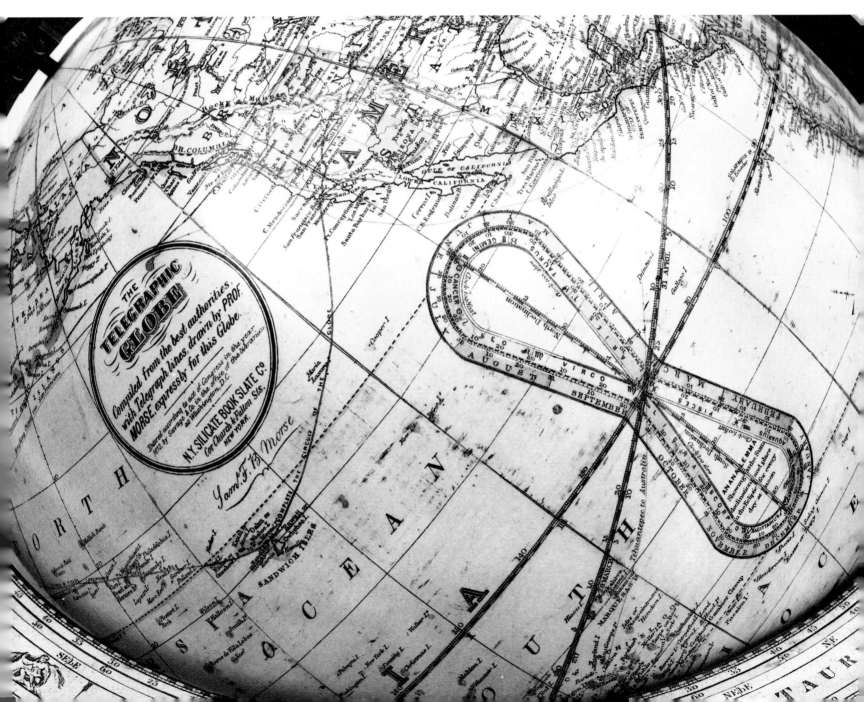

Chapter 9

CENTRAL EUROPE:

A new View of the World

For centuries the technique of copper engraving had dominated the duplication methods used in globe making. In the preceding chapters we have seen how it was often difficult for a globe maker to find the capital to invest in the precious copper plates and how existing copper plates were reused repeatedly by successive makers, sometimes over a period of 50 to100 years. With the invention of the new competitive technique of lithography in 1798 by Aloys Senefelder in Munich, the traditional method

fig 73
Series of globes by the firm of Schotte

BERLIN, STAATSBIBLIOTHEK

The firm of Ernst Schotte was of great importance in the production of globes in Berlin in the second half of the nineteenth century and the beginning of the twentieth. At the end of the 1870s, this firm made terrestrial globes in nine different sizes, from a 'doll's globe' 1in (2.5 cm) in diameter to a school globe 19in (48 cm) in diameter, along with four sizes of celestial globes. This photograph shows, in the foreground, the 1½ and 3in (4 and 8 cm) globes and a tellurium containing a 4½in (12 cm) terrestrial globe. In the background are the terrestrial globes 7, 9½ and 12in (17, 24 and 31 cm) in diameter. Finally, on the right there is the Mars globe (diameter 7in/17 cm), drawn around 1900 by H. Albrecht on the basis of data from Leo Brenner and G. Schiaparelli.

of reproduction was challenged and a number of new duplication techniques began to be invented. In particular the process of multicolour map printing enabled the industry to replace the expensive hand colouring needed until then. With the introduction of these techniques globes could be produced in large editions.

Also the look of the globe changed considerably in the nineteenth century, the more so since hand in hand with the new duplication techniques different ways of constructing the stands of globes were introduced. The use of cast iron and other metals resulted in the design of stands that had little in common with the traditional wooden stand: the meridian was reduced to an adjustable semi-circle and the horizon simply disappeared [fig 73]. The removal of the horizon is telling: the globe as made in the nineteenth century had stopped being the mechanical model by which the relation between the Earth and its surroundings could be demonstrated. The new appearance of the globe reflects how in the nineteenth century, as a result of the increasing trend towards specialization in the sciences, the studies of geography and astronomy grew apart. This development was of course the result of the great progress made in both sciences through which numerous new questions were raised and new fields of research were opened up.

Geography in the first half of the nineteenth century is characterized by the rapid growth of thematic mapping, in which the worldwide distribution of a range of connected phenomena can be visualized. The earliest maps of this kind go back to the seventeenth century. The map made by Edmond Halley depicting the trade winds and monsoons (1686) and that recording the compass variation (1701) are classical examples of thematic maps. Yet, the scope of these maps is different from those made in the early nineteenth century. Halley's charts served practical navigational purposes whereas the later thematic maps were meant to discover our world on a physical, economic and social level. This difference in scope may explain why a concept such as 'isolines', already used

by Halley in his map entitled 'Curve Lines drawn over the several Seas, to shew the degrees of the Variation of the magnetical Needle, or Sea-Compass', needed to be formulated again in 1817 when Alexander von Humboldt (1769–1859) introduced the 'isotherms'. An 'isoline' then became a line that connects all points on a surface where a particular parameter, such as the mean air pressure (isobars) or the temperature (isotherms), etc. has a certain value.

Alexander von Humboldt was one of the most prolific writers and travellers of the nineteenth century [pl 46]. His travels took him to remote places in Siberia and the Americas, where he collected all sorts of valuable data on volcanology, climatology, plant geography, geomagnetism, etc. In his life work *Kosmos* (1845 – 62), a popular book on physical cosmography with subjects ranging from mosses to galaxies, he tried to synthesize his Baconian fact-collecting programme: 'it should reflect what I have projected as my conception and vision of explored and unexplored relationships of phenomena' (Bierman, 1972, p.552). Unlike Charles Darwin (1809 – 82), who successfully combined huge amounts of data into one theory, explained in his *On the Origin of Species* (1859), Humboldt did not come up with a specific view in any of the fields he worked in. Yet, his insistence to look for global characteristics alongside local ones has stimulated and influenced the shift from the more general science of geography to the worldwide study of what are now recognized as the Earth sciences. His influence is most notable in the great *Physikalischer Atlas* of Heinrich Berghaus (1797–1884), which appeared between 1845 and 1848. An English version, *The Physical Atlas*, was published almost simultaneously by Alexander Keith Johnston (1804 – 71).

plate 46

Alexander von Humboldt at the age of eighty-seven, surrounded by his books, maps, specimens and a terrestrial globe in his library. Colour lithograph after a watercolour by Eduard Hildebrandt, 1856

plate 47

Terrestrial globe with a circumference of 1 metre (diameter 12 in / 32 cm, 1879) by Merzbach & Falk and a series of six thematic globes of 40 cm circumference (diameter 5 in / 12.5 cm) by the Institut National de Géographie, Brussels

In 1875, the booksellers Henry Merzbach and Théodore Falk published a facsimile of the recently rediscovered gores of the terrestrial and celestial globes of Gerard Mercator. A few years later, they themselves produced terrestrial and celestial globes.

After Merzbach had retired, Falk founded the Institut National de Géographie in 1882. An interesting innovation of this Institute is the publication of a series of small physical-thematic terrestrial globes based on the 'normal' political design. The photograph shows the five known versions of these thematic globes next to the normal political globe. They date from between about 1890 and 1895 and are made by colour lithography. The five topics depicted are: 1) climatology, 2) isobars and winds in July, 3) hypsometry, 4) coral reefs, volcanos and earth tremors and 5) areas with permanent snow and floating ice. These very specialized topics lead us to believe that the series originally covered a wider range.

Pair of globes from the Geographisches Institut, Weimar (diameter 12in/31cm, Weimar, 1831)

VIENNA, ÖSTERREICHISCHE NATIONALBIBLIOTHEK

At the beginning of the nineteenth century, the Geographisches Institut in Weimar formed a centre for cartography in Germany. It was set up in 1791 by Friedrich Justin Bertuch (1747–1822) as 'Fürstlich Sächsische Priviligierte Landes-Industrie-Comptoir'. The first globe appeared in 1798: the 4-inch (10cm) terrestrial globe that Franz Ludwig Güssefeld (1744–1808) designed as a supplement to the Methodische Schulatlas *of A. Chr. Gaspari. After 1804, when the Geographical Institute was founded alongside the Landes-Industrie-Comptoir, it became very involved in the mass production of globes. The number of available editions of globes of various sizes increased all the time, reaching thirty-five different types in 1861. The 1-foot (31cm) globes appeared for the first time in 1810. The 1831 edition was supervised by Carl Ferdinand Weiland (1782–1847).*

Pair of globes by Joseph Jüttner and Franz Lettany (diameter 12in/31cm, Prague, 1822–24)

VIENNA, ÖSTERREICHISCHE NATIONALBIBLIOTHEK

'The benefit that a terrestrial globe offers a future geographer in his studies is so well-known in general that there is no need to discuss the fact any more here', wrote Joseph Jüttner (1775–1848) in the introduction to his instructions on the use of his terrestrial globe. He was not the first to start producing globes in Austria in the nineteenth century, but he was the first to do so successfully. Jüttner, a captain in the Austrian army, had drawn a number of military maps already when he and Lieutenant Franz Lettany (1793–1863) produced a 1-foot diameter terrestrial globe in 1822. This was followed two years later by the partner celestial globe, drawn according to the star catalogue of Johann Elert Bode (1801) and calculated for the year 1850. Lettany, who played no part in the production of the celestial globe, made another, smaller terrestrial globe in 1825. Later in 1838–39, Jüttner made globes of 24in (62cm) diameter.

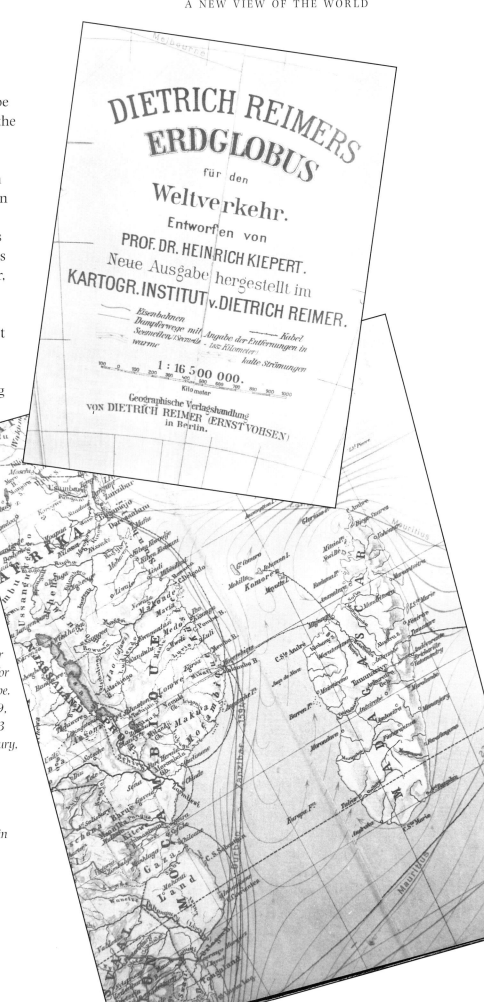

This shift in interest away from the traditional terrestrial globe created a totally new branch of globe making, the thematic globe, by which the aspect of the Earth can vary according to the topic concerned [pl 47]. The activities of Alexander von Humboldt and of Carl Ritter (1779–1859), another pioneer in thematic mapping, were particularly instrumental in stimulating the globe making industry in Germany. One of Ritter's pupils, Heinrich Kiepert, designed his first thematic globe in 1846. At the time Kiepert was working for the 'Geographisches Institut' in Weimar, which had been an important centre for the production of traditional globes since the end of the eighteenth century [pls 48 and 49]. In 1852 Kiepert joined the Berlin firm of Dietrich Reimer when they bought up the globe firm of Carl Adami. Kiepert developed for Reimer a programme for globe making which included in addition to traditional globes and traffic globes, the first geological globe [figs 74 and 75].

figs 74 and 75
**World Traffic Globe by Heinrich Kiepert
(diameter 31½in/80 cm,
Berlin; Dietrich Reimer, c.1905)**

BERLIN, FU-INSTITUT FÜR GEOGRAPHISCHE
WISSENSCHAFTEN (FACHRICHTUNG KARTOGRAPHIE)

Heinrich Kiepert (1818 – 99) started his geographical career at the Geographisches Institut at Weimar, and then worked for Dietrich Reimer, where he started by reworking Adami's globe. After this, he started to draw completely new globes. In 1879, his 21in (54 cm) terrestrial globe appeared, followed in 1883 by a 31½in (80 cm) globe. At the end of the nineteenth century, Reimer had six different terrestrial globes in his collection: a 4in (10.5 cm) people's globe, a 6in (15 cm) school globe, an 8in (21 cm) house globe, a 13½in (34 cm) school and house globe, a 21in (54 cm) school and house globe and finally the largest globe, the 'large world traffic globe', 31½in (80 cm) in diameter. In addition, Reimer also sold a relief globe 13½in (34 cm) in diameter and a 4in (10.5 cm) celestial globe.

fig76 ▽

Title of the Dutch edition of Jan Felkl's terrestrial globe
(diameter 6in/16cm, Prague, c.1870)

PRIVATE COLLECTION; PHOTO: ERIK DE GOEDEREN

The most successful globe factory in the second half of the nineteenth century was perhaps that owned by Jan Felkl (1817 – 87), based in Prague, and then in Roztok near Prague after 1870. He founded his globe factory c.1850, and soon he was offering for sale three different terrestrial globes and a celestial globe. The new Austrian Schools' law of 1870 required that every school must have a globe, and Felkl's production rose

considerably after this. In 1873 alone, he produced 15,000 globes in ten different languages. Finally, he sold globes in nine different sizes, in seventeen languages and in ten different designs. Felkl's factory did not just supply globes in the many languages that were spoken in the Austro-Hungarian Empire; he also made globes for export in English, French, Russian, Swedish, Danish, Spanish and Dutch. The globes that were not in German often gave the name of the person who provided the translation of the names. The Dutch names were provided by the teacher W. J. Geerling in Arnhem, as we can read on the text on the globe.

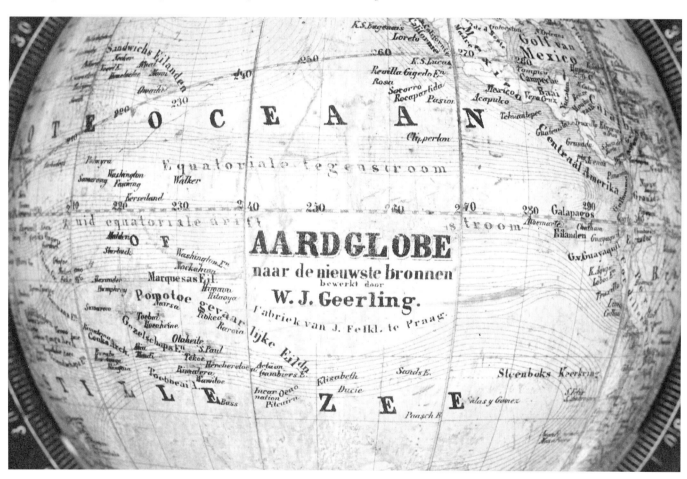

fig78 ▷

Gores for the first terrestrial globe in the Armenian language and characters
(diameter 8in/21cm, Vienna, 1838)

LONDON, ROYAL GEOGRAPHICAL SOCIETY

The Austro-Hungarian Empire consisted of such a wide divergence of peoples and languages that the world of publishing obviously worked multi-lingually. The Mechitharist Monastery

in Vienna, founded in 1810, was and still is an internationally renowned centre of Armenian culture. In 1838, one of the priests, Father Alexander Balgian, designed the gores for a terrestrial globe 8in (21 cm) in diameter, which was produced by lithography by Joseph Czerny. This was followed seven years later by the corresponding celestial globe. A larger terrestrial globe followed in 1848 – a copy, in Armenian, of Jüttner's 24in (62cm) terrestrial globe [see caption to pls 50 and 51].

fig 77 ▷

Russian terrestrial globe by A.K. Zalesskaja
(diameter 6½in/17 cm, Moscow, *c.*1870)

VIENNA, PRIVATE COLLECTION

*'Educational appliances factory "Working with Schools" of
A.K. Zalesskaja in Moscow' is the title on this terrestrial globe.
Hardly anything is known about the factory of Anastasia
Karlovna Zalesskaja, apart from a catalogue dating from 1912 of
globes and other teaching aids that the firm could supply. Before
the Revolution in 1917, Russian cartography never reached the
levels of Central and Western European countries, and they
produced hardly any globes of their own. There were only a few
predecessors to this Moscow globe factory; the most active seems
to be the 'Workshops attached to the commission of instituting
people's schools' in St Petersburg which produced pairs of globes
8in (20 cm) in diameter (1785 – 86) and 16in (41 cm) in 1793.*

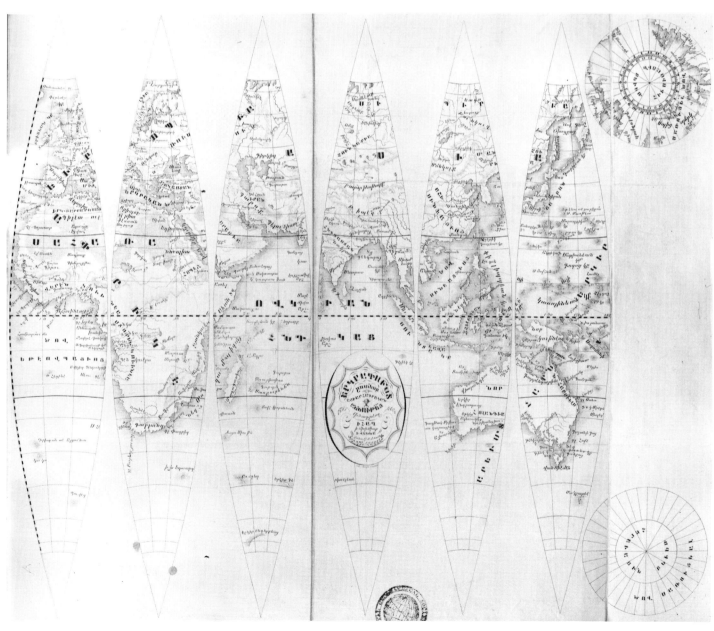

The increasing demand for teaching equipment at schools and universities also gave rise to new branches of globe making. The traditional terrestrial school globe was manufactured in many countries and in many languages [figs 76, 77 and 78]. In Berlin the firm Ernst Schotte & Co. produced globes of all sorts. Their catalogue offered terrestrial globes in thirteen sizes, that could be ordered in fourteen different languages, as well as celestial globes, lunar globes, globes of Mars and telluria [see fig 73]. In Vienna globes were manufactured initially by the publisher of maps and atlases Tranquillo Mollo (1767–1837) [fig 79]. From 1840 the market was controlled by the firm founded by Franz Leopold Schön(n)inger (1790–1877), a book binder from Vienna, and continued by his sons Joseph (1819–82) and Franz Xaver (1820–97) [fig 80]. In Prague Joseph Jüttner (1775–1848), an Austrian army officer, published globes in cooperation with Franz Lettany (1793–1863) [pls 50 and 51]. However, the main globe manufacturer of the Austrian-Hungarian monarchy was the firm of Jan Felkl (1817–87). Through the use of lithography his production of globes increased from 800 a year in 1855 to 15,000 a year in 1870 [pl 52]. The firms of Schotte in Berlin, Schön(n)inger in Vienna and Felkl in Prague certainly count among the most successful continental globe makers. Then so common, their globes are nowadays very rare: they were not considered worth conserving.

The nineteenth century also saw the decline of the traditional pair of globes, this was the result of the decreasing demand for the celestial globe. Since the pioneering work of William Herschel (1738–1822) at the end of the eighteenth century astronomical research had shifted from the solar system to the starry sky. The 'Milky Way', the broad band in the sky, which had been depicted on celestial globes for centuries, now became an object of serious study. It was discovered that the Milky Way was a flat disk of innumerable stars. The number of stars depicted on a nineteenth-century celestial globe usually does not exceed 10,000. This is but a small fraction of the total of 324,198 stars that by 1859 was recorded in the so-called *Bonner Durchmusterung* by Friedrich Argelander (1799–1875). Moreover, one of the most attractive features of a celestial globe, the constellation figures, was omitted altogether during the nineteenth century.

fig 79
**Celestial globe by Tranquillo Mollo
(diameter 8in/21cm, Vienna, 1825)**

VIENNA, UNIVERSITÄTSBIBLIOTHEK

*Tranquillo Mollo (1767 –1837), who worked in Vienna from
1798 as a publisher of maps and atlases, was inspired by the
success of the terrestrial globe of Jüttner and Lettany [pl 50], and
published a terrestrial globe in 1824. With a diameter of 8in
(21cm), this globe was considerably smaller than its model, but
it was obviously a great success, since, just under a year later
in 1825, it was followed by a celestial globe of the same size,
and by two smaller pairs of globes in the next few years
(5 and 4in/14 and 10.5cm).*

From the time of Vopel and Mercator in 1551, astronomers and cartographers had continued to add new constellation figures so that around 1800 their number had increased from the classical 48 Ptolemaic ones to 128. The sky had become so crowded with them that it became impossible to use them for scientific purposes. More importantly, the instrumental development of practical astronomy allowed stars to be located by their precise coordinates rather than by their location within a constellation. Obviously, the practical use of the constellations had come to an end. Finally, the need for astronomical knowledge in daily life or in navigation had been considerably reduced by the advanced technology used to measure time. For all these reasons the interest in nineteenth-century celestial globes diminished [pl 53].

In contrast to the decreasing fortunes of the celestial globe, there was renewed interest in making lunar and planetary globes. The idea of making a lunar globe had been put forward previously in 1647 by Johannes Hevelius in his famous *Selenographia.* The first to build a lunar globe was Christopher Wren (1632–1723), but this globe in relief is now lost. Tobias Mayer was the next scientist who contemplated the production of a lunar globe, but it was only within the development of the instrument making trade in England that in 1797 the oldest still extant lunar globe was produced by John Russell (1745–1806). In the nineteenth century lunar globes were produced more often. A remarkable lunar globe was made by Wilhelmine Witte (*b.* Böttcher 1777–1854), the mother-in-law of Johann Heinrich Mädler (1794–1874), a German astronomer who in cooperation with the rich Berlin banker Wilhelm Beer published the famous *Mappa Selenographica* (1834). In Vienna Joseph Riedl von Leuenstern designed and produced commercially lunar globes [pl 54 and fig 81]. The first lunar globe

fig 80

Terrestrial globe by Joseph Riedl von Leuenstern, published by Franz Leopold Schöninger (diameter 9in/23 cm, Vienna, 1869)

VIENNA, ÖSTERREICHISCHE NATIONALBIBLIOTHEK

The geographer Joseph Riedl, Edler von Leuenstern (1786–1856) worked in Vienna at the art, music and map publishing house owned by Joseph Schreyvogel, whom he succeeded in 1814. Riedl was responsible for the publication of maps and atlases. Schreyvogel commissioned the bookbinder Franz Leopold Schöninger (1790–1877) to produce, in 1815, a terrestrial globe 9in (23 cm) in diameter. After firstly continuing to work for Joseph Jüttner, Schöninger published globes for himself from about 1840. Under his son Franz Xaver Schönninger (1820–97) – he spelt his name with two 'n's – the production of globes reached new heights. Around 1870, they were producing some 15,000 globes a year. The company was dissolved in 1887.

based on data obtained by the new technique of photography was probably produced in the United States [fig 82]. In France the well-known popularizer of astronomy, Camille Flammarion (1842–1925) designed not only globes of the Moon, but also of Mars which were published by the firm Bertaux in Paris. Also a globe of Mars made by Hans Busk of Trinity College has been preserved [pl 55]. In our space age planetary globes have become quite common, the more so since space science has made it possible to view and depict the reverse side of the Moon, which had obviously to remain empty on the earlier globes. Against these later developments early examples of planetary globes are rare documents of celestial cartography.

In the nineteenth century the traditional pair of terrestrial and celestial globes as it was introduced in the Renaissance ceased to exist. New techniques and new images of the world at large have surpassed them in their traditional function to depict our universe. However, the globe as an educational instrument is still in use, even though it has lost its decorative function. Now as well as in the past the globe remains a much beloved symbol of the world we live in. For that reason globes are and will always be fascinating impressions of science and culture.

plate 52 ▷
German terrestrial globe by Felkl
(diameter 6in/16 cm, Roztok near Prague, *c.*1877)

VIENNA. PRIVATE COLLECTION

Globe no. 4 from the factory of Jan Felkl & Son [fig 76] had a diameter of 6in (16 cm). The author of the map on the globe is Otto Delitsch (1821–82), a professor of geography at the University of Leipzig who drew globes for Felkl from about 1860 onwards.

plate 53 △

**Celestial globe without constellations
by Carl Rohrbach
(diameter 4in/10.5 cm, Berlin;
Dietrich Reimer, 1896)**

VIENNA, PRIVATE COLLECTION

*The only celestial globe produced by Dietrich
Reimer is a modest 4in (10.5 cm) in
diameter. The stars are printed in black and
joined to each other by brown lines, so that
the constellations can be recognized. The
names of the stars and constellations are in
German. The author of the globe is the
astronomer Carl Rohrbach (1861–1932)
from Gotha, who also wrote four pages of
instructions for use.*

◁ *plate 55*

Globe of Mars by Hans Busk
(diameter 8in/21 cm, Cambridge, 1873)

CAMBRIDGE, WHIPPLE MUSEUM OF THE HISTORY OF SCIENCE

Captain Hans Busk of Trinity College, Cambridge, made this
globe of Mars on a scale of 1 inch to 450 miles for his college in
March 1873.

◁ *plate 54 and fig 81* ▽

**Lunar globe by Joseph Riedl von Leuenstern,
published by F.L. Schöninger
(diameter 9½in/24cm, Vienna, 1849)**

VIENNA, ÖSTERREICHISCHE AKADEMIE DER WISSENSCHAFTEN;
COLOUR PHOTO: LICHTBILD WERKSTÄTTE ALPENLAND

*A new development in the nineteenth century was the
commercial production of globes of the Moon. These had one
major disadvantage: the other side of the Moon can never be seen.
In order to avoid using unprinted gores, an explanatory text or a
title was often used to fill in the dark side. One of the first
commercially published lunar globes dates from 1849 and was
produced by the Viennese firm F.L. Schöninger. The title is* Der
Mond nach der orthographischen Karte von Beer und
Mädler dargestellt von Riedl von Leuenstern. Wien 1849.
There is an alphabetical list of names with the globe.

fig 82 ▷

**Lunar globe by Charles B. Boyle
(New York, before 1869)**

PHOTO: WASHINGTON, D.C., NATIONAL MUSEUM OF AMERICAN
HISTORY/SMITHSONIAN INSTITUTION

*This special hand-made model of the Moon was made by the New
York artist Charles B. Boyle, who also developed photographic
lenses, a submarine telescope and a binocular telescope. Apart
from his own observations, he referred to photographs taken by
Rutherford, Draper, DeLaRue and Whipple. Boyle's lunar globe
won first prize at the American Institute Fair of 1869. It is the
only known lunar globe from nineteenth-century America.
Its present whereabouts are unknown.*

161

BIBLIOGRAPHY

General

DER GLOBUSFREUND:
Wissenschaftliche Zeitschrift für Globen- und Instrumentenkunde (Journal for the Study of Globes and related Instruments Vienna, since 1951 annual). Index of globe makers mentioned in nos.1– 40, compiled by Rudolf Schmidt and Heide Wohlschläger in no.40/41 (1992), pp.165 –99

DEKKER, Elly
Der Himmelsglobus: Eine Welt für sich, *Focus Behaim Globus* (Nuremberg, 1992), vol. 1, pp.89 –100

FAUSER, Alois
Ältere Erd- und Himmelsgloben in Bayern (Stuttgart, 1964)

FAUSER, Alois
Kulturgeschichte des Globus (Munich, 1973)

FIORINI, Matteo
Sfere terrestri e celesti di autore Italiano oppure fatte o conservate in Italia (Rome, 1899)

KING, Henry C. (with John R. Millburn)
Geared to the stars: The evolution of Planetariums, Orreries and Astronomical Clocks (Toronto, 1978)

KROGT, Peter van der
Old globes in the Netherlands: a catalogue of terrestrial and celestial globes made prior to 1850 and preserved in Dutch collections (Utrecht, 1984)

KROGT, Peter van der
'Globes, made portable for the pocket', *Bulletin of the Scientific Instrument Society,* no.7 (1985), pp.8 –15

LANMAN, Jonathan L.
'Folding or collapsable terrestrial globes', *Der Globusfreund*, no.35/37 (1987), pp.39 – 44

MURIS, Oswald, & Gert SAARMANN
Der Globus im Wandel der Zeiten: Eine Geschichte der Globen (Berlin, 1961)

SHIRLEY, Rodney W.
The Mapping of the World: Early printed world maps 1472 –1700 (London, 1983). The Holland Press Cartographica Series; vol.9

STEVENSON, Edward Luther
Terrestrial and celestial globes: their history and construction including a consideration of their value as aids in the study of geography and astronomy (New Haven, 1921, reprinted 1971)

WARNER, Deborah J.
The Sky Explored: Celestial Cartography 1500 –1800 (New York and Amsterdam, 1979)

ZINNER, Ernst
Deutsche und niederländische astronomische Instrumente des 11.-18. Jahrhunderts, second revised edition (Munich, 1967)

Catalogue

Katalog der Ausstellung von alten Globen aus fünf Österreichischen Privatsammlungen (Österreichische Nationalbibliothek, Vienna, 1977) *Der Globusfreund*, no.24

Globen aus Urgrossvaters Zeit: Jan Felkl und seine Zeitgenossen (Österreichische Nationalbibliothek, Vienna, 1982) *Der Globusfreund*, no.30

Projections of Earth and Space: Globes and spheres from three centuries (Iparművészeti Múzeum, Budapest, 1989)

Die Welt in Händen: Globus und Karte als Modell von Erde und Raum (Staatsbibliothek Preussischer Kulturbesitz, Berlin, 1989)

Focus Behaim Globus (Germanisches Nationalmuseum, Nuremberg, 1992) 2 vols

Chapter 1

AMEISENOWA, Zofia

The globe of Martin Bylica of Olliusz and Celestial Maps in the East and West. Translated by Andrzej Potocki (Warsaw, 1959)

DURAND, Dana Bennet
The Vienna Klosterneuburg Map Corpus: A study in the transition from Medieval to Modern Science (Leiden, 1952)

HARLEY, J.B., & David WOODWARD (Ed.)
The History of Cartography, vol. I: Cartography in Prehistoric, Ancient, and Medieval Europe and the Mediterranean (Chicago and London, 1987)

HARTMANN, J.
'Die astronomische Instrumente des Kardinals Nikolaus Cusanus', *Abhandlungen der Königlichen Gesellschaft der Wissenschaften zu Göttingen, Math.-Phys. Klasse, N.F. no. 10,* (1919)

SAVAGE-SMITH, Emilie
Islamicate Celestial globes: Their history, construction and use (Washington, 1985)

TOOMER, G.J.
Ptolemy's Almagest (London, 1984). Books VII and VIII

VALERIO, Vladimiro
'Historiographic and numerical notes on the Atlante Farnese and its celestial sphere', *Der Globusfreund*, no.35/37 (1987), pp.97–124

Chapter 2

DEKKER, Elly

Johannes Schöner and the first printed celestial globe (in preparation)

DEKKER, Elly, & Peter van der KROGT
De globes van Gerard Mercator, Mercator: Tijd en Ruimte, Antwerp (forthcoming)

LINDNER, Klaus
'German globe makers especially in Nuremberg and Berlin', *Der Globusfreund*, no.35/37 (1987), pp.169–90

MURAD III
The Murad III Globes. Special appendix to Christie's Catalogue 4635, auction 30 October 1991. Research and assistance in the preparation: Gerard Turner, Elly Dekker, Julian Raby and Priscilla Thomas

WALLIS, Helen M.
'The first English globe: a recent discovery' and 'Further light on the Molyneux globes',
The Geographical Journal, no.117 (1951), pp.275 – 90 and 121 (1955), pp.304 – 11

Chapter 3

DAVIDS, C.A.
Zeewezen en wetenschap: De wetenschap en de ontwikkeling van de navigatietechniek in Nederland tussen 1585 en 1815 (Dieren, 1986)

DEKKER, Elly
'Early Explorations of the Southern Celestial Sky', *Annals of science*, no. 44 (1987), pp.439 – 70

KROGT, Peter van der
Globi Neerlandici: The production of globes in the Low Countries (Utrecht, 1993)

SCHÖFFER, I
'The Batavian Myth during the sixteenth and seventeenth centuries', in J.S. Bromley and E.H. Kossmann (eds) *Britain and the Netherlands, vol.v: Some political Mythologies. Papers delivered to the fifth Anglo-Dutch Historical Conference* (The Hague, 1975), pp.78 –101

Chapter 4

BONASERA, Francesco
'Der italienische Kosmograph Amanzio Moroncelli (1652 –1719)', *Der Globusfreund*, no.4 (1955), pp.17 –19

BONELLI, M.L.
I globi di Vincenzo Coronelli: Catalogo dei globi antichi conservati in Italia Fasc. 2 (Florence, 1960)

KROGT, Peter van der
Globi Neerlandici: The production of Globes in the Low Countries (Utrecht, 1993)

WALLIS, Helen
V. Coronelli Libro dei Globi 1693 (1701), Theatrum Orbis Terrarum: Series of facsimile atlases (Amsterdam, 1969), 4th Ser.; vol. 5

WOODWARD, David
The Holzheimer Venetian globe gores of the sixteenth century (Madison, 1987). Booklet accompanying a facsimile of a set of gores, ascribed to Giulio and Livio Sanuto

Chapter 5

AUGARDE, J.-D.
'La fabrication des instruments scientifiques au XVIIIe siècle et la corporation des fondeurs' in Chr. Blondel [et al.] (eds) *Studies in the History of Scientific Instruments* (London, 1989), pp.52 – 72

PASTOUREAU, Mireille
'Les Hardy -père et fils- et Louis-Charles Desnos "faiseurs des globes" à Paris au milieu du XVIIIe siècle' in Chr. Blondel [et al.] (eds) *Studies in the History of Scientific Instruments* (London 1989), pp.73 – 82

PELLETIER, Monique
'From the luxury item to the current consumption product: development of French globe publishing in 18th-19th centuries', *Der Globusfreund*, no.35/37 (1987), pp.131 – 44

Chapter 5 (Addendum)

BRATT, Einar
'Anders Åkerman: Ein Schwedischer Globenmacher des 18. Jahrhunderts', *Der Globusfreund* , no.9 (1960), pp.8 –12
'Thematische Züge auf schwedischen Erdgloben des 18. Jahrhunderts', *Der Globusfreund*, no.15/16 (1967), pp.87 – 95

Chapter 6

BERLIN, Isaiah
Personal impressions (London, 1980)

DÖRFLINGER, Johannes
'Deutsche Erdgloben an der Wende vom 18. zum 19. Jahrhundert', *Der Globusfreund*, no.25/27 (1978), pp.241– 58

FAUSER, Alois
'Lebensdaten von Nürnberger Globenmachern von späten 18. bis zur Mitte des 19. Jahrhundert', *Der Globusfreund* , no.31/ 32 (1983), pp.123 – 28

PILZ, K.
600 Jahre Astronomie in Nürnberg (Nuremberg, 1977)

WILSON, Curtis
Johann Gabriel Doppelmayer, in the *Dictionary of Scientific Biography*, edited by C. C. Gillispie, vol.4 (New York, 1972), pp.166 – 67

Chapter 7

BROWN, Olivia
'The instrument-making trade', *Science and profit in the 18th century* (Exhib. cat.: Whipple Museum of the History of Science, Cambridge, 1985), pp.19–24
GEE, Brian
'The Newtons of Chancery Lane and Fleet Street revisited: part 1: A question of establishment', *Bulletin of the Scientific Instrument Society*, no.35 (1992), pp.3 – 6

KEITH, Thomas
A *New Treatise on the Use of Globes or a philosophical view of the Earth and the Heavens*, third edition, corrected and improved (London, 1811)

MILLBURN, John R.
'Patent agents and the Newtons in 19th-century London', *Bulletin of the Scientific Instrument Society*, no.20 (1989), pp.3 – 6

MILLBURN, John R. (with Henry C. KING)
Wheelwright of the Heavens: The life and work of James Ferguson FRS (London, 1988)

MILLBURN, John R., & Tor E. RÖSSAAK
'The Bardin Family, globe-makers in London, and their associate, Gabriel Wright', *Der Globusfreund*, no.40/41 (1992), pp.21 – 57

SIMPSON, A.D.C.
'Globe production in Scotland in the period 1770–1830', *Der Globusfreund, no.35/37* (1987), pp.21–32

TYACKE, Sarah
London map-sellers 1660-1720 (Tring, 1978)

WALLIS, Helen
'The place of globes in English education, 1600–1800', *Der Globusfreund*, no.25/27 (1978), pp.103–10

Chapter 8

BEDINI, Silvio A.
Thinkers and Tinkers: Early American men of science (New York, 1975)

FITZ, Ellen E.
Hand-book of Terrestrial Globe; or Guide to Fitz's New Method of Mounting and Operating Globes (Boston, 1876). The quotation is taken from a letter by David and Yola Cotteen, published in the *Bulletin of the Scientific Instrument Society*, no.33 (1992) p.31. See also the letter by John R. Millburn, published in the *Bulletin of the Scientific Instrument Society*, no.34 (1992) p.29

WARNER, Deborah Jean
'The geography of heaven and earth', *Journal of the American Scientific Instrument Enterprise* , no.2 (1987), pp.14–32, 52–64, 88–104 and 147–52

Chapter 9

BIERMAN, Kurt-R.
'Friedrich Wilhelm Heinrich Alexander von Humboldt', in the *Dictionary of Scientific Biography*, edited by C.C. Gillispie, vol.6 (New York, 1972), pp.549–55

DÖRFLINGER, Johannes
'Printed Austrian globes (18th to early 20th centuries)', *Der Globusfreund*, no.35/37 (1987), pp.191–210

FISCHER, Karel
'Beiträge zur Geschichte der Mondgloben', *Der Globusfreund*, no.15/16 (1967), pp.103–22

MUCHA, Ludvík
'Geschichte und Liste der modernen tschechischen Globen', *Der Globusfreund*, no.21/23 (1973), pp.234–42

ROBINSON, Arthur H.
Early thematic mapping in the history of cartography (Chicago, 1982)

SCHANDL, Hadmar Carl
'Wiener Globenerzeugung der ersten Hälfte des 20. Jahrhunderts', *Der Globusfreund*, no.11 (1962), pp.75–79

WOHLSCHLÄGER, Heide, & Johannes DÖRFLINGER
'Österreichische und deutsche Globenhersteller der zweiten Hälfte des 19. und des beginnenden 20. Jahrhunderts', *Der Globusfreund*, no.30 (1982), pp.9–40

WAWRIK, Franz
'Mond- und Marsgloben', *Information [der] Int. Coronelli-Gesellschaft*, no.4 (March 1981), pp.II–IV, 1–15

SPHERICAL COORDINATE SYSTEMS

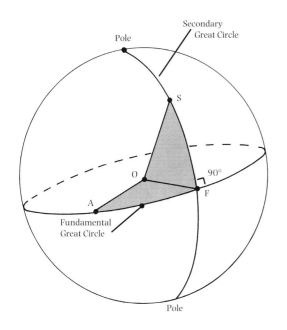

COORDINATES ON A SPHERE

ANGULAR MEASURES

The location of a point on a sphere is mathematically fixed by an orthogonal coordinate system defined by a fundamental great circle and its poles and a secondary great circle which goes through the poles and the point concerned. The angular coordinates of a point S are the arc AF and the arc SF, measured in degrees. The arc AF is the angular distance of the point F from a suitable point of origin A, measured along the fundamental great circle. The arc SF is the angular distance from the point S to the fundamental great circle, measured along the secondary great circle. It is counted positive and negative on either side of the fundamental great circle.

THE TERRESTRIAL SPHERE

LONGITUDE AND LATITUDE ON EARTH

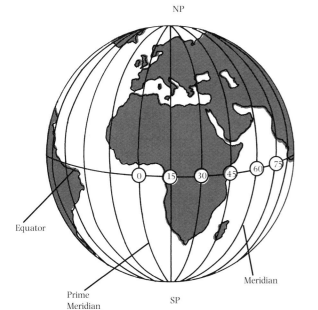

The terrestrial coordinates are defined by choosing the Earth's equator as the fundamental great circle. The north and south poles then of course are fixed by the Earth's polar axis. The secondary great circles are called meridians, and the meridian which passes through the origin is called the prime meridian. Nowadays it is the meridian which passes through Greenwich. The geographical longitude of a place is the arc along the equator, measured from the point of origin to the intersection of the meridian through that place and the equator.
The geographical latitude of a place is the arc measured along the meridian between the place and the equator.

THE CELESTIAL SPHERE

CELESTIAL LONGITUDE AND LATITUDE

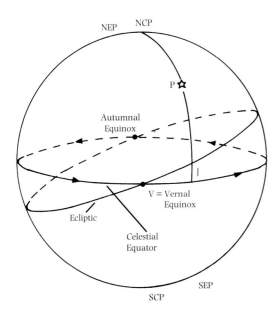

One set of celestial coordinates is defined by choosing the ecliptic, the great circle in the sky along which moves the sun in its yearly motion, as the fundamental great circle. The great circles joining the north and south ecliptic poles are then the secondary great circles and the suitable point of origin is the so-called vernal equinox. This vernal equinox is the intersection of the ecliptic with the equator. The ecliptic longitude of a star is the arc VJ, measured along the ecliptic from the vernal equinox to the intersection of the secondary great circle through the location of the star concerned with the ecliptic. The ecliptic latitude of a star's location is the arc PJ, measured along the secondary great circle, between the location of the star and the ecliptic.

THE CELESTIAL SPHERE

RIGHT ASCENSION AND DECLINATION

Another set of celestial coordinates is defined by choosing the extension of the Earth's equator, the celestial equator, as the fundamental great circle. The north and south celestial poles are then of course the extensions of the Earth's north and south poles. The secondary great circles are called hour circles, and the point of origin is again the vernal equinox, the intersection of the equator and the ecliptic. The right ascension of a star is the arc VJ, measured along the equator from the vernal equinox to the intersection of the hour circle through the location of the star concerned and the equator. The declination of a star is the arc PJ, measured along the hour circle, between the location of the star and the equator.

LIST OF GLOBE MAKERS

This survey of globe makers gives the names and some biographical details of over 400 globe makers. Included are the authors, publishers and engravers of printed globes; and all known makers of manuscript globes of the fifteenth and sixteenth centuries, and those who have made several manuscript globes in the later centuries.

The list is compiled mainly from the works of Stevenson, Zinner, Muris & Saarmann, the issues of *Der Globusfreund,* several national inventories of old globes and auction catalogues. Despite this, we are sure it is incomplete.

Abbé, Cleveland (1838 – 1916) *New York.*
Mathematician, astronomer, globe maker.

Abbott, Gorham Dunner (1807– 74) *New York.*
Patent for an inflatable globe 1868.

Abel, Carl Caspar *Nuremberg.*
Director Klinger's firm from 1852.

Adami, Carl (1802 – 74) *Berlin.*
Teacher and cartographer, his firm was continued by D. Reimer.

Adams, George (1709 – 72) *London.*
Instrument maker.

Adams, George, Jr (1750 – 95) *London.*
Instrument maker.

Adams, Dudley (1762 – 1830) *London.*
Globe and mathematical instrument maker.

Addison, John (*fl.*1825– 50) *London.*
Engraver and globe maker, worked *int.al.* for Malby.

Aeuer, Heinrich (*fl.*1825 – 30) *Elberfeld.*
Made manuscript globes, second quarter of the nineteenth century.

Aidynian, Father Arsen *Vienna.*
Author Armenian language globe 1848.

Ainslie, John (1745 – 1828) *Edinburgh.*
Surveyor and engraver.

Åkerman, Anders (1723– 78) *Uppsala.*
Globe maker, cartographer and engraver of the Cosmographical Society.

Akrel, Carl Fredrik (1779 – 1868) *Stockholm.*
Cartographer, son of following. Made globes with J. Hofgren, early nineteenth century.

Akrel, Fredrik (1748 – 1804) *Stockholm.*
Engraver, successor of Åkerman.

Albrecht, H. *Berlin.*
Author Mars globe 1898, published by Schotte.

Alessandri, Innocente *Rome.*
Engraver of Viani's globes, 1784.

American Globe & School Supply Co.
Seneca Falls, N.Y.
Publisher, 1890s.

American School Apparatus Co.
New York.
Publisher, *c.*1865 – 75.

André, Aimé (*fl.*1814 – 43) *Paris.*
Bookseller.

Andreae, Johann Ludwig (1667 – 1725) *Esslingen–Nuremberg.*
Theologian and mathematician, made globes from *c.*1710.

Andreae, Johann Philipp (*c.*1700 – after 1757) *Nuremberg–Schwabach.*
Mathematician, son of the aforementioned.

Andrews & Co., A.H. *Chicago.*
Firm, founded by Alfred H. Andrews in 1866, *fl.*up to the 1890s.

Andriveau-Goujon *Paris.*
Publishing firm, founded by Gilbert G.B. Andriveau (*c.*1805 – 80), son-in-law of M. Goujon, successors: Eugene Andriveau-Goujon (1832 – 97) and J. Andriveau-Goujon, later also Sauret-Andriveau.

Anich, Peter (1723 – 66) *Oberperfuss (Tyrol).*
Cartographer and instrument maker.

Annin, William B. (*d.*1839) *Boston.*
Patent for globe 1826, engraver for Loring and Joslin.

Apian, Philip (1531 – 89).
Mathematician and cartographer, made a large terrestrial globe in 1576, forms a pair with the celestial globe by Arboreus.

Arboreus, Heinrich *Munich.*
Jesuit, professor of physics at Ingolstadt University, made a large celestial globe in 1575, forms a pair with the terrestrial globe by Apian.

Aspheris, Petrus.
Made a bronze celestial globe *c.*1580.

Bailly, Robert de (*fl.*1525 – 30).
Engraver and metal worker, made metal terrestrial globes.

Bald(e)wein, Eberhard (*d.*1593) *Marburg.*
Instrument maker of Count William IV, worked together with Hermann Diepel.

Bale, see Woodward.

Balgian, Father Alexander *Vienna.*
Author Armenian language globes 1838 – 48.

Baradelle, Jacques-Nicolas (1701 – after 1770?) *Paris.*
Published globe gores, early eighteenth century.

Bardin, William (*c.*1740 – 98) *London.*
Globe maker, first associated with G. Wright. He made also globes for Harrison & Co.

Bardin, Thomas M. (1768 – 1819) *London.*
Associated with his father William in the globe makers firm, his successor was his son-in-law Samuel S. Edkins.

Basso (Pellicioni, Pilizzoni), Francesco (*fl.*1560 – 70) *Milan.*
Cartographer and instrument maker, constructed metal terrestrial globe in 1570.

Bastien, Ainé (*fl.*1830 – 40) *Paris.*
Publisher.

Bate, R.B. (*fl.*1800 – 49).
Mapseller, instrument maker and publisher.

Bauer, Carl Johann Sigmund (1780–1857) *Nuremberg.* Engraver and globe maker, son of J.B. Bauer.

Bauer, Johann Bernard (1752–1839) *Nuremberg.* Instrument maker.

Bauer, Peter (1783–1847) *Nuremberg.* Globe maker, son of J.B. Bauer.

Behaim, Martin (1459–1507) *Nuremberg.* Merchant, constructed the oldest extant terrestrial globe (1492).

Benci, Carlo (1616–76). Sylvestrian monk, made manuscript globes.

Beringer, David (1756–1821) *Nuremberg.* Instrument maker, published the first edition of the Bode/Sotzmann globe pair.

Berndt, Johann Christoph (1707–98) *Nuremberg.* Engraver of the gores of a reduction of Pigeon's great globe (now lost).

Bernoulli I, Johannes (1647–1748) *Basel.* Physician, author of Bruckner's first globe (1722).

Berra, Marco *Prague.* Publisher; folding globe 1842.

Berry, Miles, see Newton.

Berry, William (*fl.*1669–1708) *London.* Engraver, bookseller and publisher; collaborated with Morden.

Bertaux, Emile (*fl.c.*1880–1900) *Paris.* Publisher of *int.al.* globes of Dien, Dubail, Eichens's navisphere, Mars and lunar globes.

Bertuch, Friedrich Justin (1747–1822) *Weimar.* Geographer, founder Landes-Industrie-Comptoir.

Betts, John (*fl.*1844–63) *London.* Published, produced collapsible terrestrial globes, from *c.*1860.

Beyer, F. Golden terrestrial globe of 1568.

Beyer, Johann (1673–1751) *Hamburg.* Instrument maker, made concave celestial globes in two hemispheres.

Biller, Bernhard, Sr & Jr (*fl.*mid-nineteenth century) *Vienna.* Engravers, worked for Jüttner and Schöninger, *c.*1839–44; engraved the first Hungarian language globe 1840.

Bion, Nicolas (1652–1733) *Paris.* Geographer and instrument maker.

Blaeu, Willem Jansz. (1571–1638) *Amsterdam.* Cartographer and publisher.

Blaeu, Joan (*c.*1598–1673) *Amsterdam.* Son and successor of W.J. Blaeu.

Bliss, Sylvester. Author Outline Globe by Jewett and Joslin 1851.

Bode, Johann Elert (1747–1826) *Berlin.* Astronomer, globes published by Beringer and Franz.

Böhm, Joseph Georg (1807–68) *Innsbruck–Prague.* Astronomer, celestial globe 1846, worked also for Felkl.

Boisseau, Jean (*fl.*1631–48) *Paris.* Publisher, copied several Dutch globe gores.

Boncompagni, Hieronymo de. Italian cartographer, celestial globe *c.*1570.

Bonne, Rigobert (1727–95) *Paris.* Author terrestrial globe, published by J. Lattré.

Boulengier, Louis *Lyon.* Astronomer and geographer, made a set of terrestrial globe gores, *c.*1514, probably maker of so-called Jagiellonic Gold Globe and of the Lenox Globe.

Bretel, A. Designer of Eichens's navisphere with A. Hue, *c.*1880.

Brown & Peirce. Publishers of a pocket globe, *c.*1835.

Bruckner, Isaac (1689–1762) *Basel.* Geographer and instrument maker.

Buache, Philippe (1700–73) *Paris.* Geographer and publisher, son-in-law and successor of Delisle.

Buache de la Neuville, Jean-Nicholas (1741–1825) *Paris.* Geographer, nephew of Ph. Buache, published a globe together with Bonne.

Bühler, Johann Adam (1813–70) *Nuremberg.* Engraver of Klinger's globes.

Bürgi, Jost (1552–1632). Swiss mathematician, astronomer and clockmaker, constructed several metal celestial globes for Count William IV of Hesse.

Buy de Mornas, Claude (*d.*1783) *Paris.* Historian and geographer, author globes of Fortin.

Campbell, Stillman P. *Buffalo.* Tellurians with small globes 1867.

Campe, Friedrich (*d.*1846) *Nuremberg.* Publisher, *int.al.* Bauer's globes.

Cartaro, Mario *Rome.* Cartographer and engraver, *fl.*1560–1612.

Cary family *London.* Globe makers 1791–1821: J.& W. Cary: John (*c.*1754–1835) & William Cary (*c.*1760–1825); 1821–*c.*1850: G.&J. Cary: George (*d.*1859) and John Cary (1791–1852), sons of John.

Case & Co., O.D. *Hartford, Conn.* Publisher, globe 1877.

Cassini, Giovanni Maria (*c.*1745–1824–30) *Rome.* Engraver globe gores 1790–92.

C.B., see Carl Bauer.

Cella, Philipp (*b.*1790) *München.* Published inflatable globe 1831.

Central School Supply House *Chicago.* Published globes since 1900.

Ceulen, Abraham van (*c.*1635–1707) *Amsterdam.* Brother of J. J. van Ceulen, published pocket globe in 1697.

Ceulen, Jan Jansz. van (1635–89) *Amsterdam.* Successor of Blaeu's globe workshop.

Charpentier, P. (*fl.c.*1650) *Paris.* Published sheet with engraving for armillary sphere, including small terrestrial globe gores.

Cheney Globe Co. *Seneca Falls, N.Y./Mystic, Ct.* Founded by Flavius Cheney. *fl.*1882–*c.*1900.

Coen, C. *Trieste.*
Published terrestrial globe gores 1867.

Colom, Jacob Aertsz. (1600 – 74)
Amsterdam.
Cartographer and publisher.

Columbus Verlag Paul Oestergaard
Berlin.
Publishing firm of globes, founded 1909 by
Paul Oestergaard.

**Commission of Instituting People's
Schools** *St Petersburg.*
Published two globe pairs, 1785/86 and
1793.

Copley, Charles *Brooklyn.*
Engraver, *fl.*1843 – 69.

Cornell, Silas (1789 –1864) *Rochester,
N.Y.*
Surveyor, engineer and globe maker.

Coronelli, Vincenzo (1650 –1718)
Paris–Venice.
Cosmographer, founder of the first
Geographical Society, 1680.

Costa, Giovanni Francesco (*d.*1773)
Venice. Made a globe pair for the Venice
Academy of Science, 1754.

Covens, Cornelis (1764 –1825)
Amsterdam.
Owner of Mortier Covens & Fils, who
re-published Valk's globes *c.*1800.

Cowley, John L. (*fl.*1730 – 50) *London.*
Geographer, collaborated with Thomas
Heath in the production of glass celestial
globes.

Cox, Joseph and James (early nineteenth
century) *London.*
Instrument makers, published pocket
globes.

Cram & Co., George F. *Indianapolis.*
Twentieth century.

Cruchley, George Frederick *London.*
Mapseller, globe maker and publisher,
*fl.*1823 – 76.

Cummings, Hilliard & Co. *Boston.*
Published Gardner's globe 1823.

Cushee, Leonard (early eighteenth
century) *London.*
Globe maker.

Cushee, Richard (*fl.*1729 – 32) *London.*
Surveyor and globe maker.

Cust, E. *Purey.*
Hydrographer of the Navy, 1909 –14,
invented Star Finder, published by Barker
& Son.

Czerny, Joseph *Vienna.*
Lithographer of Father Balgian's
Armenian language globe pair
1838 – 45.

Dames, W.
Author of a geological globe, published by
Reimer, early twentieth century.

Danti, Ignazio (1536 – 86) *Florence.*
Astronomer and papal cosmographer,
constructed a large terrestrial globe.

Darton & Co. *London?*
Published a pocket globe *c.*1815.

David, Johann (*fl.*1825 – 39) *Vienna.*
Engraver, worked for Lettany and Jüttner.

Davis, John (1821–1903) *Pittsburgh.*
Made tellurians and globes.

Delitsch, Otto (1821– 82).
Geographer, author Felkl's terrestrial
globes.

Delamarche, Charles-François
(1740 –1817) *Paris.*
Geographer, publisher and globe maker.

Delamarche, Félix *Paris.*
Son and successor of Charles-Fr.
Delamarche.

Delisle, Guillaume (1675 –1726) *Paris.*
Geographer.

Delure, Jean-Baptiste (early eighteenth
century) *Paris.*
Map and globe maker.

Denoyer-Geppert Co. *Chicago.*
Publishing firm, twentieth century.

Desbuissons, J.
Author Spanish globe, published by
Bertaux, *c.*1880.

Desnos, Louis-Charles (1725 – 91?)
Paris.
Instrument maker, successor of Hardy,
made globes from 1742, collaborated with
Nolin.

Deur, Johannes (1667/8 –1734)
Amsterdam.
Engraver, pocket globe 1720s.

Dezauche, J.A. (*fl.*1780 –1831) *Paris.*
Successor of Buache and Delisle.

Dien, Charles, Sr *Paris.*
Engraver, associate of Delamarche's firm
*c.*1819.

Dien, Charles, Jr (1809 – 70) *Paris.*
Astronomer, son of above, author several
celestial globes.

Diepel, Hermann (*fl.*1560s).
Goldsmith, worked together with
Baldwein. Made several metal celestial
globes.

Donaldson (& Sons), Alexander
(*fl.*1799 –1828) *Edinburgh.*
Publisher.

Doppelmayr, Johann Gabriel
(1671?–1750) *Nuremberg.*
Astronomer and cartographer, author of
globes constructed by Puschner.

Dorn, Hans (*c.*1430 –1509). Instrument
maker, celestial globe 1480 (Bylica globe).

Drentwett, Abraham.
Goldsmith, made silver globes *c.*1700.

Dreykorn, Johann Paul (1805 – 75)
Nuremberg.
Owner of Klinger's firm since *c.*1830.

Driessens, P. *Brussels.*
Publisher early nineteenth century,
published toy planetariums.

Dubail, Edmond (*b.*1851).
Author of Bertaux' terrestrial globe,
*c.*1875.

Duchetti, Claudio (1554 – 97) *Rome.*
Re-printed gores of Demongenet and
Oterschaden, late sixteenth century.

Duminger (early nineteenth century).
Lithographer, miniature globe.

Dunn, Samuel (*d.*1794) *London.*
Mathematician and publisher.

Du Val, Pierre (1619 – 82) *Paris.*
Geographer, nephew of N. Sanson, globe
gores 1666.

Edkins, Samuel S. (*c.*1791 –1853)
London.
Son-in-law and successor of T.M. Bardin,
associated with his son John Parry Edkins
(*b.*1823).

Eichens, Frederic W.
Astronomer, inventor of the 'navisphere', a celestial globe for navigation, drawn by Hue and Bretel and published by Bertaux, *c.*1880 (described by H. de Magnac in 1881).

Eimmart, Georg Christoph (1638 – 1705) *Nuremberg.*
Astronomer, globe gores 1705.

Elekes, Franz von *Vienna.*
Military cartographer, lithographer, designed Schöninger's terrestrial globe 1844.

Elfimov, P. A. *St Petersburg?*
Made a globe pair 1841 – 42.

Elzevier.
Dutch publishing firm, collapsible globe *c.*1880.

Emmoser, Gerhard (*fl.*1573 – 1579) *Vienna.*
Clockmaker, made a silver celestial globe 1579.

Endersch, Johann Friedrich (1705 – 69) *Elbing (West Prussia).*
Mathematician and cartographer.

Erben, Josef (1830 – 1910) *Prague.*
Geographer, author Felkl's globes.

Etablissement Géographique de Bruxelles.
Publishing firm, founded 1830 by Ph. Vander Maelen.

Evans & Co., R.O. *Chicago.*
School supply company, advertised globes 1899.

Excelsior School Furniture Co.
Scranton, Pa.; later Cincinnati.
Owned by Isaac Smith Wachob and later by J.C.Brooke; globes from 1870s.

Faber, Samuel (1657 – 1716).
Theologian and geographer, wrote the address to the reader of the celestial globes by J.L.Andreae.

Felkl, Jan (1817 – 87)
Prague. From 1870 Roztok near Prague.
Publisher, his firm, founded *c.*1850, became one of the largest globe publishers of the second half of the nineteenth century in Central Europe. In 1875 Jan's son Kryštof Zikmund Felkl (1855–94) was his father's companion and was the firm named Felkl & Son. After Kryštof died his older brother Ferdinand Felkl

(1846 – 1925) became owner. The firm closed down in 1952.

Felt, David *Boston.*
Published Gardner's globe 1825 – 29.

Fembo, Ch. (early nineteenth century) *Nuremberg.*
Successor of the firm of Homann's heirs.

Ferguson, James (1710 – 76) *London.*
Astronomer and geographer, re-published *int.al.* Senex's globes, 'Ferguson's globes' published by Martin and Bardin.

Field, Franklin (*c.*1824 – 1904) *Troy, N.Y.*
Globe maker, probably the Franklin globes refer to his name.

Filiberto, Emanuele.
Probably author of a terrestrial globe *c.*1570.

Finé, Oronce (1494 – 1555).
French astronomer and cartographer.

Flammarion, Camille (1842 – 1925).
Astronomer, author lunar and Mars globes *c.*1895, published by Bertaux.

Fletcher (nineteenth century).
English publisher.

Floriani, Antonio *Venice.*
Engraved world map in form of globe gores 1556.

Forest, J. (late nineteenth/early twentieth century) *Paris.*
Publisher.

Forlani, Paolo (second half sixteenth century) *Venice.*
Engraver and cartographer. Made metal terrestrial globe *c.*1560.

Fortin, Jean (1750 – 1831) *Paris.*
Publisher and instrument maker, succeeded by Delamarche.

Franklin globes, see F. Field, Merriam & Moore and H.B.Nims.

Franz, Johann Georg (*c.*1776 – 1836) *Nuremberg.*
Publisher, successor of Beringer, re-issued Bode's and Sotzmann's globes.

Frauenholz *Nuremberg.*
Sold globes of Klinger, 1790. His imprint on some copies of 32 cm celestial globe.

Fremin, A.R. (*fl.*1820 – 68) *Paris.*
Geographer, author Bastien's terrestrial globe.

Frese, W. de *Copenhagen.*
Author Felkl's globes.

Freytag & Berndt, G. *Vienna.*
Publishing firm founded 1879, globes from 1907.

Friedrich, Ernst (*fl.c.*1900).
Author Columbus's traffic globe.

Frisius, Gemma (1508 – 55) *Louvain.*
Mathematician and geographer.

Fuchs, M.C.B.(eighteenth century).
Made coni-globes of northern and southern celestial sky.

Fürst, Paul (*c.*1605 – 66) *Nuremberg.*
Publisher, re-issued Oterschaden's and Habrecht's gores mid-seventeenth century.

Gair, Robert (1839 – 1927) *New York.*
Paper product manufacturer, globes from 1890s.

Garcia de Cespedes, Andres *Seville.*
Geographer, included terrestrial globe gores in his Regimiento de Navegación 1606.

Gardner, [James W.?].
Globes 1823 – 29, published by Cummings, Hilliard & Co. and by D.Felt.

Garthe, Dr. C.
Author 'cosmoglobes', 1827.

Geographic Educator *New York.*
Publisher of a terrestrial globe, *c.*1927.

Geerling, W.J. *Arnhem.*
Teacher, author of Felkl's globes in the Dutch language.

Gessner, Abraham (1552 – 1612) *Zurich.*
Goldsmith, made several silver globe-goblets.

Girard & Barrère (early twentieth century) *Paris.*
Publishers.

Glowczewski, W./Urania *Warsaw.*
Early twentieth century.

Gobille, Gédéon *Paris.*
Published small globe gores *c.*1650.

Goldthwaite, William M. *Chicago.*
Folding globes, 1890s, published by Gol[?]meian Globe Co.

Gönczy, Pal (1817 – 92) *Budapest.*
Author Felkl's globes in the Hungarian language.

Goode, J. Paul.
Author of Rand McNally's first physical globe, 1928.

Goodyear, Charles (1800 – 60) *USA.*
Inflatable globes *c.*1850.

Goos, Abraham (*b.*1589) *Amsterdam.*
Engraver of globe gores with Van den Keere and Janssonius.

Göpfert, E. *Annaberg.*
Author Felkl's globes.

Greuter, Matthäus (*c.*1556 – 1638) *Rome.*
Cartographer and globe maker.

Grimm, Julius Ludwig (1806 – 34) *Berlin.*
Made pneumatic globes (Pocock type).

Grosselin *Paris.*
Owner Delamarche's firm from 1847.

Grünewald, Christoph (1801 – 54) *Nuremberg.*
Engraver, *int.al.* Bauer's foldable globes.

Güssefeld, Franz Ludwig (1744 – 1808) *Weimar.*
Author globe Landes-Industrie-Comptoir.

Haack, Hermann (1872 – 1966).
Author of globes, first published 1914 by Justus Perthes in Gotha.

Haan, Friedrich Gottlieb (1771–1827) *Torgau and Dresden.*
Teacher, author of terrestrial globe *c.*1820.

Haardt, Robert (1884 – 1962).
Inventor of the 'Rollglobus' (cradle globe), 1935, published by Freytag & Berndt, Columbus, Girard-Barrère and others.

Habrecht, Isaak II (1589 – 1633) *Strassburg.*
Mathematician, author of globes constructed by Heyden.

Hahn, Philipp Matthäus (1739 – 90) *Onstmettingen-Kornwestheim.*
Made several astronomical clocks with globes, first in co-operation with Ph.G. Schaudt, later together with his eldest son Christoph Matthäus Hahn (1767 – 1833).

Hammond & Co., C.S. *New York.*
Twentieth century.

Haraeus, Franciscus (*c.*1555 – 1631) *Antwerp.*
Theologian and historian, globes *c.*1615 – 20.

Hardy, Jacques (first half eighteenth century) *Paris.*
Publisher, made globes between 1738 and 1745 together with his son Nicolas Hardy (before 1717 – 44) Paris. Nicolas's widow remarried L.-C. Desnos.

Harris & Son, Thomas (early nineteenth century) *London.*
Opticians and globe makers.

Harrison & Co., John (*fl.*1783 – 1815) *London.*
Published globes since 1783, their globes were made by Bardin.

Hartmann, Georg (1489 – 1564) *Nuremberg.*
Compass and globe maker.

Haskel, Daniel (1784 – 1848) *Brooklyn.*
Founder New York School Apparatus Co. *c.*1830.

Haspel *Schwäbisch Hall.*
Publisher, mid-nineteenth century.

Hauer, Johann (1586 – 1660) *Nuremberg.*
Engraved several metal globes (in co-operation with Jeremias Ritter), and gores for a terrestrial globe.

Heath, Thomas (1714 – 65) *London.*
Instrument maker, constructed glass globes with Cowley.

Henze, Adolf *Leipzig.*
Publisher, globe in instalments 1890–95.

Heyden, Christian (*c.*1525 – 76) *Nuremberg.*
Mathematician, made several manuscript globes.

Heyden, Gaspar van der (*c.*1496 – after 1549) *Leuven.*
Goldsmith and engraver.

Heyden, Jakob von (1573 – 1645) *Strasbourg.*
Engraver and printer of Habrecht's globes.

Heymann, Ludwig Julius *Berlin.*
Publisher, *fl.c.*1860 – 1903.

Hill, Nathaniel (mid-eighteenth century) *London.*
Surveyor and globe maker, succeeded by Thomas Bateman, who apprenticed John Newton and William Palmer.

Hofgren, J. (early nineteenth century) *Stockholm.*
Made globe with C.Fr. Akrel.

Holbrook & Co. *Berea, Ohio.*
Publisher of a.o. globes, founded by Alfred and Dwight Holbrook (sons of Josiah), 1840s.

Holbrook Apparatus Mfg. Co.;
Holbrook School Apparatus Co.
Wethersfield, Hartford, Conn.
Globe producing firm. Founded by Dwight Holbrook, 1854.

Holbrook, Charles W. *Hartford, Conn.*
Son of Dwight Holbrook, manufacturer of school supplies.

Holbrook, Dwight, see Holbrook Apparatus Mfg. Co., Holbrook & Co.

Holbrook, Josiah (1788 – 1854) *New York.*
Globe maker 1840s.

Hölzel, Eduard *Vienna.*
Publisher, globes since 1897.

Homann, Johann Baptist (1664 – 1724) *Nuremberg.*
Publisher of maps and atlases.

Homännische Erben (*fl.*1724 – early nineteenth century) *Nuremberg.*
Firm of Homann's heirs, *int.al.* Georg M.Lowitz and Ch.Fembo.

Hondius, Jodocus, Sr (1563 – 1612) *London–Amsterdam.*
Engraver and map publisher.

Hondius, Jodocus, Jr (1593 – 1629) *Amsterdam.*
Son and successor of J. Hondius, Sr.

Hondius, Henricus (1597 – 1651) *Amsterdam.*
Son and successor of J. Hondius, Sr.

Hue, A.
Designer of Eichens's navisphere with A. Bretel, *c.*1880.

Hughes & Son, H. (early twentieth century) *London.*
Publisher.

Ikelmer *Paris.*
Nineteenth century publisher of a Spanish terrestrial globe.

Institut National de Géographie (*fl.*1882 – *c.*1900) *Brussels.*
Founded 1882 by Th. Falk-Fabian (see Merzbach & Falk).

Jacob *London.*
Pocket globe by Jacob & Halse, 1809.

Jamnitzer, Christoph (1563 – 1618)
Nuremberg.
Goldsmith, made metal globes.

Janssonius, Johannes (*c.*1588 – 1664)
Amsterdam.
Publisher.

Jenig, Wolfgang Paul (*d.*1805) *Nuremberg.*
Pencil maker, published Doppelmayr's
globes *c.*1790.

Jode, Gerard de (1509 – 91) *Antwerp.*
Globe gores (*c.*1587) ascribed to him.

Johnston, W. & A. K. *Edinburgh.*
Firm founded 1825 by the engraver
William Johnston (1802 – 88), in 1826
his brother Alexander Keith Johnston
(1804 –71) joined the firm; they published
globes from mid-nineteenth century.

Jones, Thomas *Denver.*
Relief globes 1897, published by A. H.
Andrews Co.

Jones, W. & S. *London.*
William (1765 – 1831) & Samuel (active
1810) Jones, brothers, instrument makers,
globes from 1782.

Joslin, Gilman (1804 – *c.*1886) *Boston.*
Globe maker.

Jüttner, Joseph (1775 –1848)
Prague–Vienna.
Military cartographer, co-operated with
Lettany.

Juvet, Louis-Paul (1838 –1930)
Canajoharie, N.Y., Glens Falls.
Time globes from 1867.

Kaerius, Petrus, see Pieter van den Keere.

Kaiser, Jos.Fr. Graz.
Lithographic firm; dissected terrestrial and
celestial globes 1823 – 24.

Kassner, C.
Author of a meteorological globe,
published by Reimer, 1907.

Keere, Pieter van den (1571 – after 1646)
Amsterdam.
Engraver of Plancius's globes.

Kelvin & Hughes.
Star globe, early twentieth century.

Kiepert, Heinrich (1818 – 99)
Weimar–Berlin.
Geographer and cartographer.

Kirkwood (& Sons), James
(*fl.*1774 –1824) *Edinburgh.*
Publishers and engravers. One of the
sons is Robert Kirkwood, cartographer,
surveyor and engraver. He succeeded his
father in 1824.

Klegna, W. *Vienna.*
Author terrestrial globe, published by
Schöninger 1841.

Klinger, Johann Georg (1764 –1806)
Nuremberg.
Publisher.

Klinger's Kunsthandlung, J.G.
(*fl.*since 1806) *Nuremberg.*
Under this name Klinger's widow
continued the firm. From 1831 owned
by J. P. Dreykorn and since 1852 by
C.C. Abel, who changed the name to
Abel-Klinger.

Korbgeweit, Richard (1870-1910).
Author of Schotte's 'Schul- und Familien-
Globus'.

Krause, Arthur.
Author of Räth's globes.

Kretzschmar, Friedrich (*b.c.*1817)
Prague.
Engraver and lithographer, mid-
nineteenth century.

Kummer, Karl Wilhelm (1785 –1855)
Berlin.
Relief globes from 1822.

Kunsch, H. *Leipzig.*
Lithographer, author terrestrial globe
*c.*1870.

Kunst- und Industrie-Comptoir
Vienna.
Terrestrial globe 1812, second edition by
Riedl 1814.

Lade, Eduard Frhr. von (1817 –1904).
Constructed a moon globe, *c.*1860.

La Feuille, Jacques de
(1668 – before 1719) *Amsterdam.*
Mapseller, successor of Blaeu's globe
makery.

Lalande, Joseph-Jérôme de (1732 –1807)
Paris.
Astronomer, author celestial globe
published by Lattré.

Lallement, Robert.
Author lunar globe, *c.*1850.

Lancaster, Cyrus (*c.*1802 – 62)
Albany, N.Y.
Successor of J. Wilson & Sons, *c.*1835.

Lane, N. *London.*
Pocket globe 1776; also pocket globes of
the early nineteenth century are named
'Lane's globe'.

Lane, Samuel.
Constructed the first American globe,
*c.*1760.

Langlois, Hyacinthe *Paris.*
Book and globeseller, 1820s.

Langren, Jacob Floris van (*d.*1610)
Amsterdam.
Globe maker.

Langren, Arnold Floris van
(*c.*1571–1644) *Amsterdam.*
Son and successor of J.F. van Langren.

Langren, Hendrik Floris van
(*c.*1574 – 1648) *Amsterdam.*
Son and successor of J.F. van Langren.

Langren, Michael Florent van
(1598 – 1675) *Brussels.*
Son and successor of Arnold F. van
Langren.

Lapie, Pierre (1779 –1850) *Paris.*
Geographer, author Langlois' terrestrial
globes, his name also appears on the globes
by Bastien.

La Ramée, Giles de *Paris.*
Author of small terrestrial globe gores
(*c.*1650), engraved by his pupil Joan
Aquilius.

Lartigue, Pierre (1744 – before 1828)
Paris.
Made relief globes 1777.

Lattré, Jean (*fl.c.*1750 –1800) *Paris.*
Engraver and publisher globe pair by
Bonne & Lalande.

Lea, Philip (*fl.*1683 – *d.*1700) *London.*
Cartographer, globe and instrument
maker, associate with Robert Morden.

Lebègue & Cie., J. (late nineteenth
century) *Paris.*
Publisher.

Lebègue, Alphonse N. & Cie. (1814 – 85)
Brussels.
Publisher, globes *c.*1880.

Legrand, P.
Constructed wooden globes, *c.*1730.

Lettany, Franz (1793–1863) *Prague.*
Military cartographer, worked with
Jüttner.

Leuchs & Co. (early nineteenth century)
Nuremberg.
Publisher.

Levasseur, Emile (1828–1911).
Geographer, terrestrial globe *c.*1890.

L'Isle, de, see Delisle.

Lopez, Pedro Martin de *Madrid.*
Published collapsible globes 1840.

Loring, Josiah (1775–*c.*1840) *Boston.*
Publisher and bookseller.

Lothian, John (*fl.*1825–46) *Edinburgh.*
Geographer and publisher.

Lotter, Matthäus Albrecht (1741–1810)
Augsburg.
Successor of Seutter, his globe gores are
included in Homann's atlas of 1774.

Lowitz, Georg Moritz (1722–1774)
Nuremberg.
Partner of the firm of Homann's heirs.

Loysel *Paris.*
Terrestrial globe dated 1787.

Luther, C.
Cartographer of globes for Columbus-
Verlag.

Malby & Co. (*fl.c.*1840–1900) *London.*
Lithographers and publishers for the
Society for the Diffusion of Useful
Knowledge.

Mang, Adolf (1849–1933).
German author of globes, 1888 and later.

Manning, J. (*fl.*1850–60).
English(?) globe maker.

Marin & Schmidt.
Publishers inflatable globe, *c.*1838.

Martin, Benjamin (1704/5–82) *London.*
Publisher, new editions of Senex's globes.

McDermott, Francis *New York.*
Globes 1876–78.

Meder (early nineteenth century)
Heidelberg.
Publisher.

Menzies, J. *Edinburgh.*
Engraver of Kirkwood's globe 1804.

Mercator, Gerard (1512–94)
Louvain-Duisburg.
Geographer and cartographer.

Merklas, Vaclav (1809–66) *Prague.*
Publisher.

Merriam & Moore (*fl.*1851–68)
Troy, N.Y.
1851–52, publisher of Franklin globes;
from 1852–58 Merriam, Moore & Co.,
1858–68 Moore & Nims; see also Nims.

Merzbach & Falk (*fl.c.*1875–82)
Brussels.
Firm founded by Henry Merzbach
(1837–after 1892) and Theodore Falk-
Fabian (1845–after 1914); published
facsimile of Mercator's globe gores in 1875
and since *c.*1878 modern globes;
succeeded by Falk's Institut National de
Géographie.

Messier, Charles (1730–1817).
Author Delamarche's celestial globe, his
name also appears on Bastien's celestial
globe.

Miller, John (1746–1815) *Edinburgh.*
Publisher, pocket globe 1793.

Miot, Vincenzo (1712–87).
Italian astronomer, published a celestial
globe, 1710.

Mogg, Edward (*fl.*1804–48) *London.*
Publisher, dissected globe 1812.

Moll, Herman (*d.*1732) *London.*
Engraver and geographer.

Mollo, Tranquillo (1767–1837) *Vienna.*
Publisher.

Mollo, Eduard (1797–1842) *Vienna.*
Son and successor of T. Mollo.

Molyneux, Emery (*d.*1598/99) *London.*
First English globe maker (1592).

Monachus, Franciscus. *Leuven.*
Made *c.*1527 a terrestrial globe, now lost.

Mongenet, François de (*fl.*1550s).
Globe maker of Vesoul, France.

Morden, Robert (*d.*1703).
Geographer and publisher, made with
Philip Lea globe pairs.

Moroncelli, Amanzio (1652–1719).
Sylvestrian monk, made from 1672 several
manuscript globes with diameters ranging
from 27 to 200 cm.

Mortier Covens & Fils (*fl.*1794–1866)
Amsterdam.
Publishing firm of C. Covens.

Moxon, Joseph (1627–91) London.
Mathematician and globe maker.

MPS. Globes *c.*1845.

Müller, Carl *Karlsruhe.*
Engraver of Siedentopf's globe.

Murdock, David C. (1805–80) *West
Boylston, Mass.*
School suppliers since 1837, sometimes
with his brother Artemas Murdock.

Mynde, James (*fl.*1720–60).
Engraver of Ferguson's pocket globe.

Nagy, Karl (1797–1876).
Astronomer, made the first Hungarian
globe pair (1840).

Naze, Jean.
Instrument maker, constructed clock with
two metal terrestrial globes, *c.*1560.

Neuse, R.
Author of globes for Columbus-Verlag.

Neussel, Otto.
Terrestrial globe 1883.

Newton family *London (Chancery Lane).*
Family of globe makers: John Newton
(1759–1844), apprentice of Hill's
successor Thomas Bateman, started
globe production *c.*1782. From *c.*1818
partner with his son William Newton
(1786–1861): J. & W. Newton. In the
1830s Miles Berry was associate: Newton,
Son & Berry (*c.*1832–41). Later William's
son William Edward Newton (1818–79)
entered the firm: W. Newton & Son (from
*c.*1841 onwards).

Newton & Co. *London (Fleet Street).*
Instrument makers from *c.*1851. Firm of
Frederick (1824–1909) and Edward
(1829–1909) Newton, grandchildren
of Daniel Newton, younger brother of
John Newton.

New York School Apparatus Co.,
see D. Haskel.

New York Silicate Book Slate Co.
Globe 1872.

Nicolai, Gulielmus (*fl.*1573–1613) *Lyon.*
Engraver of globe gores 1603.

Nims & Co., H. B. (*fl.*1858–96)
Troy, N.Y.
Publisher of Franklin globes 1869–85
and 1890–96; from 1858–68 Moore &
Nims; 1886–89 Nims & Night; see also
Merriam & Moore.

Nolin, Jean-Baptiste, Sr (1657–1725)
Paris.
Geographer and engraver, Coronelli's
celestial globe 1688–93.

Nolin, Jean-Baptiste, Jr (1686–1762) *Paris.*
Geographer, co-operated with Desnos.

Nollet, Jean Antoine (1700–70) *Paris.*
Instrument and globe maker.

Nystrom & Co., A.J. *Chicago.*
Publisher of globes, maps and atlases.

Oestergaard, Paul (1873–1956) *Berlin.*
Founder Columbus-Verlag.

Oterschaden, Joannes (late sixteenth century) *Lyon (?).*
Engraver, globe gores.

Palmer, William.
Apprentice of Thomas Bateman. Published with John Newton a revised edition of Hill's pocket globe, *c.*1782.

Paravia & Cia., G.P. *Italy.*
Firm founded 1727, globes since *c.*1906.

Patrick & Co., T.
Pocket globe 1808.

P.B., see Peter Bauer.

Pendleton, John B. & William S. *Boston.*
Lithographers, globe 1837.

Perce, Elbert (1832–69) *New York.*
Author 'magnetic' globes, 1864.

Perigot, C. (late nineteenth century).
Globe maker.

Perthes, Justus (1739–1815) *Gotha.*
Founder of the famous publisher of maps and atlases, which started in 1914 with the production of globes.

Pestalozzi *Warsaw.*
School supplying firm, published globes in the 1920s.

Philip & Son, George (*fl.*since 1834) *London.*
Publisher first of Malby's globe, later under their own name.

Pigeon, Jean (1654–1739) *Paris.*
Globe maker.

Pisani, Ottavio (*b.*1575).
Cosmographer, constructed a metal terrestrial globe, *c.*1595.

Plancius, Petrus (1552–1622) *Amsterdam.*
Cartographer and theologian.

Platus (Plautus), Carolus (*fl.*1595–1600) *Rome.*
Constructed metal globes.

Pocock, George (1774–1843) *London.*
Inflatable globe *c.*1830.

Poirson, Jean-Baptiste (1760–1831) *Paris.*
Geographer, author terrestrial globe.

Potter, J.D. Globe pair *c.*1852.

Praetorius, Johannes (1537–1616) *Nuremberg.*
Astronomer and mathematician, constructed several metal globes.

Price, Charles (*fl.*1697–*d.*1733) *London.*
Publisher, pocket globe *c.*1711.

Pristley, F. *Moscow.*
Publisher of globes, *c.*1823.

Probst, Johann Michael, Jr (*c.*1757–1809) *Augsburg.*
Engraver and art dealer.

Puschner, Johann Georg I (1680–1749) *Nuremberg.*
Constructor of Doppelmayr's globes. His son Johann Georg II was instrument maker and published Doppelmayr's globes after 1749.

Ram, Johannes de (1648–93) *Amsterdam.*
Engraver, successor of Blaeu's globe makery.

Rand, McNally & Co. *Chicago.*
Opened 1856, globes since 1887.

Räth, Paul *Leipzig.*
Author and publisher, firm founded 1917.

R.C.A. *Rome.*
Publishing firm, re-edited Greuter's globe 1744.

Řehák, J. *Prague.*
Author Felkl's globes in the Czech language.

Reimer, Dietrich (1818–99) *Berlin.*
Publisher.

Reinhold, Johann (*fl.*1584–92) *Augsburg.*
Made several metal globes, mostly with Georg Roll.

Renaud, H. *Brussels.*
Author of the globes of the Etablissement Géographique de Bruxelles.

Repogle, Luther I. *Chicago.*
Founder of the Repogle firm, from 1931.

Riedig, Christian Gottlieb (1768–1853).
Author terrestrial globes.

Riedig, M.
Author of globes published by Schreibers Erben in Leipzig.

Riediger, Johann Adam (1680–1756).
Swiss surveyor and military cartographer, made glass globes.

Riedel, Joh.
Author of globes for Columbus-Verlag.

Riedl (von Leuenstern), Joseph (*fl.*1810–50) *Vienna.*
Cartographer, author of Schöninger's globes.

Riem, Johannes.
Author celestial globe Columbus-Verlag.

Ritter, Jeremias *Nuremberg.*
Goldsmith, made metal globes with Johann Hauer.

Robert de Vaugondy, Didier (1723–86) *Paris.*
Geographer and publisher, son and successor of Gilles Robert de Vaugondy.

Rohrbach, Carl (1861–1932). Author of Reimer's celestial globe.

Roll, Georg (*d.*1592) *Augsburg.*
Clock and instrument maker, made several metal globes together with Johann Reinhold.

Rolph, Smith & Co. (late nineteenth century) *Toronto.*
Engravers of a terrestrial globe for the Education Department of Ontario.

Romer, Eugeniusz (1871–1954) *L'vov.*
Cartographer and publisher.

Romstet, Christian (1640–1721) *Leipzig.*
Published copies of Van den Keere's globes.

Rosa, Vincenzo.
Italian globe maker, constructed several large manuscript terrestrial globes 1793.

Rossi, Giovanni Battista de (active 1640–72) *Rome.*
Publisher, re-edited Greuter's globes.

Rossi, Giuseppe de *Rome.*
Publisher, re-edition Hondius's globes 1615.

Rothaug, Johann Georg (1850 –1924)
Vienna.
Geographer and cartographer, author
globes by Freytag & Berndt.

Ruggles, Steven P.
Constructed in 1837 a globe for the blind.

Russell, John (1745 –1806). Made lunar
globe in 1797.

Salziger, Johann Peter (*d.*1853)
Nuremberg.
Publisher, globes *c.*1850.

Santa Cruz, Alonso de (*c.*1500 – 72).
Spanish cartographer, drew manuscript
globe gores 1542.

Sanuto, Giulio & Livio (*c.*1520 – 76)
Venice.
Brothers, engraver and geographer
respectively, made globe gores *c.*1574.

Sauret-Andriveau.
Publishing firm, see Andriveau-Goujon.

Scaltaglia, Pietro *Rome.*
Engraver of Viani's globes, 1784.

Schaudt, Philipp Gottfried (1739 –1809)
Onstmettingen.
School teacher and instrument maker,
made planetarium together with
Ph. M. Hahn.

Scheda, Joseph von (1815 –99) *Vienna.*
Cartographer, lithographer of the
Armenian language globe 1848.

Schedler, Joseph (*fl.c.*1850 – 80)
Jersey City.
Globe manufacturer.

Schedler, Herman.
Successor of Joseph Schedler.

Scherer, Heinrich (1628 –1704)
München.
Jesuit, professor of mathematics, included
in his Atlas Novus of 1700 a sheet with
terrestrial globe gores.

Schiaparelli, G. *Milan.*
Author Felkl's Italian globes.

Schickard, Wilhelm, Jr *Tübingen.*
Nephew of the astronomer and map maker
Wilhelm Schickard (1592 –1635).
Published concave celestial coni-globes.

Schiepp, Christoff *Augsburg.*
Engraver, brass terrestrial globe *c.*1535.

Schissler, Christoph (*c.*1530 –1609)
Augsburg.
Instrument maker. Large copper celestial
globe.

Schissler, Christoph, Jr (before 1561 –
after 1625). *Augsburg, Vienna, Prague.*
Clockmaker. Metal, clockwork driven
celestial globe.

Schneeweiss, Urban[?] (end sixteenth
century) *Dresden.*
Goldsmith, constructed metal celestial
globe *c.*1575.

Schneider, Franz J. P. (*b.*1818)
Hannoversch Münden.
Terrestrial globe 1843.

Schniep, Ulrich (second half sixteenth
century) *Munich.*
Instrument maker. Pair of globes
1575 – 77.

Schöner, Johann (1477 –1547)
Bamberg / Nuremberg.
Mathematician, astronomer and
cosmographer.

Schöninger, Franz Leopold (1790 –1877)
Vienna.
Publisher, started with publishing globes of
Klegna and Elekes, later he published
under his own name

Schön(n)inger, Franz Xaver (1820 – 97)
Vienna.
Son and successor of F. L. Schöninger.

Schöninger, Joseph (1819 – 82) *Vienna.*
Son and successor of F. L. Schön(n)inger.

Schotte & Co., Ernst *Berlin.*
Publishing firm, founded 1855.

Schreibers Erben (early nineteenth
century) *Leipzig.*
Publisher, in 1814 sold to Schropp.

Schropp & Co., Simon (1757 –1817)
Berlin.
Publisher.

Scott, Robert.
Author of Kirkwood's terrestrial globe
1804.

Schulz, Friedrich *Stuttgart.*
Publisher of folding globes, *c.*1830.

Selander, N. *Stockholm.*
Globe producer, 1927.

Selss, Eduard (*fl.*1841– 43) *Coesfeld.*
Globe maker.

Senex, John (*d.*1740) *London.*
Cartographer and engraver, *fl.*1702 – 40.

Seutter, Georg Matthäus (1678 –1757)
Augsburg.
Publisher of maps and atlases.

Siedentopf, F. *Karlsruhe.*
Publisher, globe 1825.

Smit, Pieter Maasz. *Amsterdam.*
Published 1698 a book *Cosmographia* with
instructions for globe making, the book
includes gores for a terrestrial globe.

Smith, C., & Son (late nineteenth century)
London.
Publisher.

Sotzmann, Daniel Friedrich (1754 – after
1819) *Berlin.*
Geographer, author of terrestrial globes
published by Beringer and Franz.

Spano, Antonio (*d.*1615).
Italian cartographer and engraver, made
ivory terrestrial globe in 1593.

Spirincx, Nicolaus *Lyon.*
Engraver of a set of celestial and terrestrial
globe gores, 1610.

Stampfer, Jakob (*c.*1505 –79) *Zurich.*
Goldsmith and engraver, made silver
terrestrial globe *c.*1539.

Stanford, Edward *London.*
Geographical publisher, sold *int.al.* Malby's
globes, produced by Philip & Son.

Stella, Tilmann (1525 – 89) *Wittenburg.*
Geographer and cartographer, author
celestial globe 1555.

Stöffler, Johann (1452 –1531) *Justingen.*
Professor of mathematics at the University
of Tübingen.

Stokes, William.
Published 'mnemonical' globe, 1868.

Sturm, Anton (1788 –1827) *Vienna.*
Teacher at Military Engineering Academy;
folding globe 1823.

Suchard, Ph. (late nineteenth century).
Globe maker, probably French.

Suchecki, M. *Warsaw.*
Author Felkl's globes in the Polish
language.

Tardieu, Ambroise (1788 –1846) *Paris.*
Cartographer and engraver, inflatable
globe 1830s.

Thomas, G. (late nineteenth century) *Paris.*
Publisher.

Tisley, Samuel Charles *London.*
Globe maker 1860s.

Tomšič, I. *Ljubljana.*
Author Felkl's globes in the Slovenian language.

Townsend, Dennis (1817 – 74) *Felchville, Vermont.*
Folding globe 1869.

Tuttell, Thomas *London.*
Instrument maker, *c.*1700.

Urania *Katowice.*
Early twentieth century.

Valk, Gerard (1652 –1726) *Amsterdam.*
Engraver and publisher.

Valk, Leonard (1675 –1746) *Amsterdam.*
Son and successor of G. Valk.

Vander Maelen, Philippe (1795 –1869) *Brussels.*
Geographer, founder Etablissement Géographique de Bruxelles (1830).

Veen, Adriaen (*b.c.*1572) *Amsterdam.*
Globe pair with J. Hondius, Jr 1613.

Viani, Matteo (*d.*1789) *Venice.*
Publisher of globes 1784.

Villanova, D.J. *Madrid.*
Author Felkl's globes in the Spanish language.

Vivien de St Martin, Louis (1802 – 97) *Paris.*
Geographer.

Volpaia (Euphrosynus Vulpius or Ulpius), Eufrosino della (*d.*1552).
Instrument maker.

Vopel, Kaspar (1511– 61) *Cologne.*
Cosmographer, professor of mathematics.

Wagner & Debes *Leipzig.*
Publishers of 'Langes Erdgloben', up to *c.*1940.

Waldseemüller, Martin (1470 – *c.*1520) *St Die.*
Cosmographer, author of the first printed globe *c.*1507.

Waligórski, F. *L'vov.*
Author Felkl's globes.

Weber Costello *Chicago.*
Publisher of globes, maps and atlases.

Weigel, Erhard (1625 – 99) *Jena.*
Made several celestial globes with constellations derived from heraldry, all metal.

Weigel, Johann Christoph (1654 –1725) *Nuremberg.*
Publisher, re-edited Habrecht's globe.

Weiland, Carl Ferdinand (1782 –1847) *Weimar.*
Author terrestrial globe of the Weimar Geographical Institute.

Weimar, Geographisches Institut.
Founded 1804.

Weimar, Landes-Industrie-Comptoir, Fürstlich Sächsische Privilegierte.
Founded 1791 by F.L. Bertuch.

West Bazaar *London.*
Publisher, pocket globe, *c.*1800.

Weygand, Fr. J. *The Hague and Amsterdam.*
Dissected globe *c.*1825.

Wilson, James (1763 –1855) *Bradford, Vt.; Albany, N.Y.*
Globe maker, later with his sons John and Samuel.

Winter, Kaspar *Vienna.*
Publisher; terrestrial globe 1840.

Woodward G.; Bale & Woodward *London.*
Publishers, *c.*1850.

Wright, Gabriel (*d.*1803/04) *London.*
Instrument and globe maker with Bardin firm.

Wyld, James (1812 – 87) *London.*
Cartographer, author of giant globes constructed by the Georama firm, 1850.

Zalder, V. *Slany near Kladno (Bohemia).*
Publisher; terrestrial globe 1848.

Zalesskaja, Anastasia Karlovna (nineteenth century) *Moscow.*
Publisher of school supplies.

Zeune, Johann August (1778 –1853) *Berlin.*
Geographer, made relief globes for the blind.

Zimmermann, Johann Jacob (1644 – 93).
Professor of mathematics in Heidelberg. Published a coni-globe in 1692.

Zumbach de Coesfelt, Lotharius (1661–1727) *Leiden.*
Astronomer and mathematician, assisted in the globe production of G. Valk.

INDEX

Figures in *italics* refer to captions on the page concerned